Introduction to

Statistical Optics

This book is in the

ADDISON-WESLEY SERIES IN ADVANCED PHYSICS

Morton Hamermesh, *Consulting Editor*

Introduction to
Statistical Optics

by
EDWARD L. O'NEILL
Department of Physics, Boston University

ADDISON-WESLEY PUBLISHING COMPANY, INC.

Reading, Massachusetts · Palo Alto · London

To Dave, Donna, and Lee

Preface

Optics is an old and venerable branch of physics. Thus, one may reasonably question the need for a book such as this. The answer lies simply in the fact that the field has recently undergone a renaissance, and that in the process much progress has been made in the diffraction theory of image formation. However, these advances have not yet found their way into the texts used for the conventional undergraduate courses in optics. Although this book describes some recent developments in optics, it is not designed for such a course, *per se*. However, since several chapters are self-contained, the material can be easily incorporated into the curriculum. The text is aimed principally at both senior and first-year graduate students in physics, and at communications engineers in industry.

Much of the material first appeared as a set of lecture notes distributed by the author during a seminar at Boston University in the summer of 1956. Since that time, the material has been revised, updated, and reprinted in several forms. With growing interest in the field and demands for these notes continuing, it was decided to rewrite the manuscript from the beginning. While much of the specialized treatment of the effects of the various aberrations on the optical frequency response has remained intact, it was decided to approach the subject in a language in which both the graduate student in physics and the communications engineer would feel equally at home. Hence Chapters 1 and 2 describe, in some detail, the role of the Green's function in mathematical physics and the essential differences between spatial and time filters. Chapter 3 contains a brief review of the fundamental relations of paraxial optics, using the compact and efficient matrix notation for the translation and refraction operations. Chapters 4, 5, and 6 describe the effects of the various aberration terms on image formation from the standpoint of both physical and geometrical optics. Up to this point, a more accurate title for the book might be *Communication Theory and Image-Formation Optics*. However, it was further decided to include statistical descriptions both of the scenes that often confront optical instruments and of the light itself in scalar and vector form. Strictly speaking, the book represents an introduction to *classical* statistical optics. The subject of quantum statistical optics, still an area of active research, requires, I believe, a completely separate, more sophisticated and more modern treatment than that offered here. However, it is hoped that the student will be better prepared to cope with the intricacies of quantum optics by mastering the mathematical techniques of this more familiar field.

It is neither possible nor appropriate to pay tribute here to the many predecessors who have provided the background for this work. However, it is with pleasure that I acknowledge the extent to which I was originally attracted to this field by the works of Professor André Maréchal of the Institute d'Optique in Paris and Professor H. H. Hopkins of Imperial College, London. It is with equal pleasure that I acknowledge the influence of Professor Emil Wolf whose ideas so pervaded my later thinking. More concretely, I wish to thank Professor Peter Elias, of the Massachusetts Institute of Technology, in whose department I spent the 1960–1961 academic year as a guest compiling the major part of the manuscript. I am also grateful to Dr. Willem Brouwer for permission to condense sections of his own manuscript in order to present geometrical optics in the compact and economical matrix form. In addition, I wish to express my gratitude to one of my graduate students, Mr. Arwind Marathay, who will shortly pursue a career of his own in physics, for taking time out from his own researches to write Chapter 9, without which, I believe, the book would not have been complete.

Finally, while every teacher owes a debt to all his students, I should like to thank, in particular, Mr. John DeVelis for proofreading the manuscript and for helping in so many ways to bring it to completion.

Needham, Mass.   E. L. O'N.
November 1962

Contents

Chapter 6. ANALYSIS AND SYNTHESIS

Chapter 7. STATISTICAL METHODS

Chapter 8. MATRIX AND COHERENCE THEORY

Chapter 9. THE THEORY OF PARTIAL POLARIZATION

Appendix A. FOURIER-BESSEL SERIES AND INTEGRALS

Appendix B. PROBABILITY AND ENTROPY THEORY

INDEX

1

Green's Function and Linear Theory

1-1 Linear second-order differential operators

Physicists and engineers are well aware of the advantages of describing fields by linear equations. In such a representation the effect of independent sources is additive. Unfortunately, with the rapid growth of science and technology and the accompanying pressure for specialization, certain basic properties of linear theory sometimes are overlooked. For example, that which the electrical engineer calls the *impulse response* is the *spread function* to the optical physicist, and the *Green's function* to the field theorist. A causality requirement in one discipline is a dispersion relation in another and a condition for a physically realizable network in a third.

With only a slight appeal here to the operational calculus, we wish to demonstrate [from a discussion based on the classical theory of second-order linear differential equations] in simple, yet quite general, terms how the integral representing the principle of linear superposition arises. Consider then the system represented by the differential operator D and for which $x(t)$ represents the driving function and $y(t)$ the response (Fig. 1-1). For example, for a damped mechanical oscillator (Fig. 1-2),

$$D = m\frac{d^2}{dt^2} + R\frac{d}{dt} + k,$$

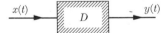

FIGURE 1-1

and the way in which the system responds to $x(t)$ is described by

$$Dy(t) = x(t). \qquad (1\text{-}1)$$

With no attempt to justify its existence yet, we hypothesize that an inverse operator D^{-1} exists such that $D^{-1}D = 1$. Then at least formally we can write

$$y(t) = D^{-1}x(t). \qquad (1\text{-}2)$$

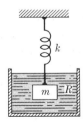

FIGURE 1-2

1

This is the type of solution we are seeking, for *given* $x(t)$, we wish to determine $y(t)$. As a special case of the driving function $x(t)$, we choose a sharp impulse applied at t' which is described by the Dirac function $\delta(t - t')$. We now *define* its response as the Green's function $g(t, t')$, so that

$$Dg(t, t') = \delta(t - t'). \tag{1-3}$$

In the following discussion, it is important to note that D and D^{-1} operate on the variable t; t' merely describes the location of the impulse. Inverting Eq. (1-3), we have,

$$g(t, t') = D^{-1}\,\delta(t - t'). \tag{1-4}$$

Among its other peculiar properties, the Dirac function is defined in such a way that it can sift out a single ordinate in the form

$$x(t) = \int_{-\infty}^{+\infty} \delta(t - t')x(t')\,dt'.$$

Substituting this expression into Eq. (1-2), we get

$$y(t) = \int_{-\infty}^{+\infty} D^{-1}\,\delta(t - t')x(t')\,dt'$$

which, by virtue of Eq. (1-4), can be written as

$$y(t) = \int_{-\infty}^{+\infty} g(t, t')x(t')\,dt',$$

and hence we see the significance of the inverse integral operator D^{-1}. If the response of the system is insensitive to a translation of the time axis, then $g(t, t')$ must be of the form $g(t - t')$. Furthermore, if the causality condition is to be obeyed so that $g(t - t') = 0$ for $t < t'$, then we can write

$$y(t) = \int_{-\infty}^{t} g(t - t')x(t')\,dt'$$

which indicates that we can look into the past and then add up the contributions to the present, but not into the future. This result is well known to people who are familiar with linear filter theory.

However, there are several unsatisfactory aspects to this approach. In addition to the facts that D^{-1} is not well defined and the boundary conditions of the problem are not explicitly stated, one could add the homogeneous solution of Eq. (1-1) to the right side of Eq. (1-2) and still have a perfectly acceptable solution.

Let us start, therefore, with a fresh approach based on the classical theory of linear differential equations [1].* Consider the homogeneous equation

$$L(u) = a_2(x) \frac{d^2u}{dx^2} + a_1(x) \frac{du}{dx} + a_0(x)u = 0 \qquad (1\text{–}5)$$

We now define the *adjoint* equation (for a reason that will soon be clear)

$$\widetilde{L}(v) = \frac{d^2}{dx^2}(a_2v) - \frac{d}{dx}(a_1v) + a_0v = 0,$$

such that

$$vL(u) - u\widetilde{L}(v) = \frac{dP(u, v)}{dx}$$

is a perfect differential. *P* is called the *bilinear concomitant* and is given by

$$P(u, v) = a_1uv + a_2v \frac{du}{dx} - u \frac{d}{dx}(a_2v). \qquad (1\text{–}6)$$

As a result of these machinations, we can write

$$\int_a^b [vL(u) - u\widetilde{L}(v)]\, dx = [P(u, v)]_a^b.$$

We now distinguish two cases.

1–2 Self-adjoint operators

An operator is said to be self-adjoint if $\widetilde{L} = L$. Therefore, setting

$$(a_2u)'' - (a_1u)' + a_0u = a_2u'' + a_1u' + a_0u$$

or

$$2a_2'u' + a_2''u - a_1'u = 2a_1u',$$

we see that $L(u)$ is self-adjoint if

$$a_1(x) = \frac{da_2(x)}{dx}.$$

That is, the differential operator

$$L(u) = \frac{d}{dx}\left(a_2 \frac{du}{dx}\right) + a_0u$$

is self-adjoint. To cast this into a more recognizable form, we make the

---

* The numbers in brackets are keyed to the references at the end of the chapters.

substitutions

$$a_2(x) = p(x), \qquad a_0(x) = q(x),$$

and we see that the second-order linear self-adjoint operator

$$L(u) = \frac{d}{dx}\left(p\,\frac{du}{dx}\right) + qu = \widetilde{L}(u) \tag{1-7}$$

is the Sturm-Liouville [2] differential operator. Furthermore, for this case, the bilinear concomitant takes on the particularly simple form

$$P(u, v) = p(vu' - uv').$$

The Sturm-Liouville equation plays such a central role in the theory of spectral decomposition that we shall digress a bit here and note that if $v = u^*$, the basic eigenvalue equations arising in the boundary value problems of mathematical physics can be written as

$$L(u_n) = -\lambda_n w(x) u_n(x), \qquad \widetilde{L}(u_m^*) = -\lambda_m^* w(x) u_m^*(x),$$

where u_n and λ_n are the eigenfunctions and eigenvalues, respectively, of the operator L, and $w(x)$ is a positive weighting function characteristic of the coordinate system being used. Multiplying the first eigenvalue equation by u_m^*, the second by u_n, subtracting and making use of Eqs. (1–6) and (1–7), we get

$$(\lambda_m^* - \lambda_n)\int_a^b u_n u_m^* w(x)\,dx = \left[p(x)\left\{u_m^*\,\frac{du_n}{dx} - u_n\,\frac{du_m^*}{dx}\right\}\right]_a^b$$

$$= \int_a^b [u_m^* L(u_n) - u_n \widetilde{L}(u_m^*)]\,dx.$$

For the boundary value problems for which the function or its slope vanishes at the boundary, the right-hand side is zero which results in

$$\int_a^b u_m^* L(u_n)\,dx = \int_a^b u_n \widetilde{L}(u_m^*)\,dx$$

and

$$\int_a^b u_n u_m^* w(x)\,dx = c^2 \delta_{mn}. \tag{1-8}$$

The first relation states that L is Hermitian, and the second is the orthogonality condition† for the set of functions u_n with respect to the weighting

---

† We are assuming here that the eigenvalues are nondegenerate, that is, that

$$\lambda_m \neq \lambda_n.$$

function $w(x)$. By absorbing the constant c, the functions can also be normalized. Finally, for $m = n$, $\lambda_n^* = \lambda_n$ so that the eigenvalues are real.

1-3 Nonself-adjoint operators

Returning to the question of adjointness, we now seek, by the proper integrating factor, to cast all equations of the form of Eq. (1–5) into the self-adjoint form. Therefore, multiplying Eq. (1–5) by

$$\frac{1}{a_2} e^{\int (a_1/a_2)\, dx},$$

we get

$$L_1(u) = e^{\int (a_1/a_2)\, dx} \left[u'' + \frac{a_1}{a_2} u' + \frac{a_0}{a_2} u \right] = 0.$$

By defining

$$p(x) = e^{\int (a_1/a_2)\, dx}, \qquad q(x) = \frac{a_0}{a_2} e^{\int (a_1/a_2)\, dx},$$

we can write

$$L_1(u) = \frac{d}{dx}\left(p\,\frac{du}{dx} \right) + qu = 0$$

so that $L_1(u)$ is self-adjoint. Hence all linear second-order differential operators can be cast into the self-adjoint form.

1-4 The inhomogeneous equation

With this background developed, let us now direct our attention to the solution of the inhomogeneous differential equation

$$L(u) = \rho(x), \tag{1-9}$$

where $\rho(x)$ describes some source function. Following earlier procedures we now define $g(x', x)$ by the equation

$$L(g) = \delta(x - x') = \tilde{L}\tilde{g}(x, x'). \tag{1-10}$$

We now multiply Eq. (1–9) by g, Eq. (1–10) by u, subtract and integrate.† The result is

$$\int [gL(u) - uL(g)]\, dx = \int_a^b g(x', x)\rho(x)\, dx - \int_a^b u(x)\, \delta(x - x')dx.$$

Now making use of the sifting property of the Dirac function and the mean-

---

† We are making use of the fact here that $\tilde{g}(x, x') = g(x', x)$.

ing of P, we have

$$u(x') = \int_a^b g(x', x)\rho(x)\, dx - [P(u, g)]_a^b,$$

$$\tag{1-11}$$

where

$$P(u, g) = p(gu' - ug').$$

We see then that by choosing a Green's function that obeys the *same* boundary conditions as u, the second term on the right-hand side of Eq. (1–11) can be made to vanish. Further, if the result is insensitive to a shift of the coordinate axis, we can write

$$u(x') = \int_a^b g(x' - x)\rho(x)\, dx.$$

Physically, this is an especially pleasing result, for it says that each point in the source function $\rho(x)$ is spread out in the form $g(x' - x)$, and the resulting disturbance $u(x')$ is a linear superposition over all source points. Further, this result holds for both space and time variations and can readily be extended to handle two- and three-dimensional time varying fields [3].

1–5 Determination of the Green's function

The crucial point now is to determine the Green's function. This can be a study in its own right. We confine our attention here to two special cases: that of constant coefficients and that of the self-adjoint Sturm-Liouville differential equation.

Constant coefficients.

$$L(g) = a_2 g'' + a_1 g' + a_0 g = \delta(x - x').$$

$$\tag{1-12}$$

We now expand $\delta(x - x')$ and $g(x - x')$ in a Fourier integral

$$\delta(x - x') = \frac{1}{2\pi} \int_{-\infty}^{+\infty} e^{i\omega(x-x')}\, d\omega,$$

$$g(x - x') = \frac{1}{2\pi} \int_{-\infty}^{+\infty} G(\omega)e^{i\omega(x-x')}\, d\omega.$$

$$\tag{1-13}$$

Substituting these integrals into Eq. (1–12), we have

$$\int_{-\infty}^{+\infty} G(\omega)[-\omega^2 a_2 + i\omega a_1 + a_0]e^{i\omega(x-x')}\, d\omega = \int_{-\infty}^{+\infty} e^{i\omega(x-x')}\, d\omega,$$

which determines $G(\omega)$ and hence $g(x - x')$ in the form

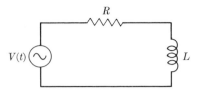

FIGURE 1–3

$$g(x - x') = \frac{1}{2\pi} \int_{-\infty}^{+\infty} \frac{e^{i\omega(x-x')}}{a_0 - \omega^2 a_2 + ia_1\omega} \, d\omega. \qquad (1\text{--}14)$$

Here we will not enter into a discussion of how one chooses the path of integration [4] in the complex plane to satisfy causality, stability, and hence boundary conditions on $g(x, x')$. Later we shall discuss these matters when comparing space versus time filters.

As an illustration of the approach, consider a simple R-L circuit (Fig. 1–3). The Green's function (impulse response) is determined by quickly opening and closing a switch at $t = t'$ so that

$$L\frac{dg}{dt} + Rg = \delta(t - t'),$$

$$g(t, t') = 0, \qquad t < t'.$$

Making the appropriate substitutions in Eq. (1–14), we have

$$g(t - t') = \frac{1}{2\pi} \int_{-\infty}^{+\infty} \frac{e^{i\omega(t-t')}}{R + i\omega L} \, d\omega.$$

Here, it is sufficient to say that we take the inverse Laplace transform in place of the Fourier transform to insure that $g(t - t') = 0$ for $t < t'$. The result*

$$g(t - t') = \frac{1}{L} e^{-(R/L)(t-t')}, \qquad t \geq t',$$

$$= 0, \qquad\qquad t < t'.$$

As a filter, the frequency response is given by inverting Eq. (1–13) in the form

$$G(\omega) = \frac{1}{R + i\omega L} = |G(\omega)| e^{i\theta(\omega)},$$

where (Fig. 1–4)

$$|G(\omega)| = \frac{1}{\sqrt{R^2 + \omega^2 L^2}}, \qquad \theta(\omega) = \tan^{-1}\frac{\omega L}{R}.$$

---

* In the superposition integral, of course, $g(t, t')$ appears in the folded form.

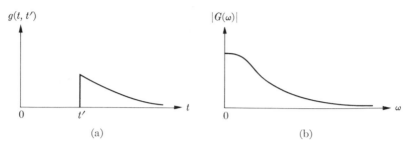

FIGURE 1–4

Sturm-Liouville differential equation. With reference to the orthogonal character of the solutions of the homogeneous S-L equation demonstrated in Eq. (1–8), we now attempt to solve

$$Lg + \lambda wg = \delta(x - x') \tag{1-15}$$

by expanding $g(x, x')$ and $\delta(x - x')$ into a series of $\psi_n(x)$, where

$$L\psi_n = -\lambda_n w(x)\psi_n,$$

which is the solution of the homogeneous S-L equation. For the Dirac function, we have

$$\delta(x - x') = \sum_n D_n(x')\psi_n(x),$$

where

$$D_n(x') = \psi_n^*(x')w(x')$$

from the orthogonality of the $\psi_n(x)$.

Since $\delta(x - x')$ is a real symmetric "function" of x and x', we have

$$\delta(x - x') = \sum_n \psi_n^*(x')\psi_n(x)w(x') = \sum_n \psi_n(x)\psi_n^*(x')w(x).$$

In a completely analogous fashion, we expand

$$g(x, x') = \sum_n C_n(x')\psi_n(x)$$

and substitute these expressions into Eq. (1–15), such that

$$\sum_n C_n(x')[L\psi_n + \lambda w\psi_n] = \sum_n \psi_n^*(x')\psi_n(x)w(x).$$

But by virtue of the fact that $L\psi_n = -\lambda_n w\psi_n$, we get

$$C_n(x') = \frac{\psi_n^*(x')}{\lambda - \lambda_n},$$

so that finally

$$g(x, x') = \sum_n \frac{\psi_n(x)\psi_n^*(x')}{\lambda - \lambda_n}.$$

As an elementary illustration of how these methods can be extended to more than one dimension, we shall consider the Poisson equation of electrostatics. In mks units, this equation reads

$$\nabla^2 V = -\frac{\rho(x, y, z)}{\epsilon_0},$$

where V is the electrostatic potential due to a volume density of charge $\rho(x, y, z)$. The Green's function satisfies the equation

$$\nabla^2 g(\mathbf{r} - \mathbf{r}') = -\frac{\delta(\mathbf{r} - \mathbf{r}')}{\epsilon_0},$$

where

$$\delta(\mathbf{r} - \mathbf{r}') = \delta(x - x')\,\delta(y - y')\,\delta(z - z')$$

is a symbolic representation of an isolated point-charge in space. The potential at (x', y', z'), due to a point charge at (x, y, z), is well known to be

$$g(\mathbf{r} - \mathbf{r}') = \frac{1}{4\pi\epsilon_0 R},$$

where

$$R = \sqrt{(x - x')^2 + (y - y')^2 + (z - z')^2}.$$

Thus by the principle of linear superposition, the potential $V(x', y', z')$,

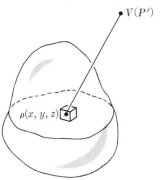

FIGURE 1–5

due to the distribution of charge $\rho(x, y, z)$ (Fig. 1–5), is given by

$$V(P') = \iiint g(\mathbf{r}, \mathbf{r}')\rho(\mathbf{r}) \, d\mathbf{r}$$

$$= \frac{1}{4\pi\epsilon_0} \iiint \frac{\rho(x, y, z) \, dx \, dy \, dz}{\sqrt{(x - x')^2 + (y - y')^2 + (z - z')^2}} .$$

1–6 The principle of linear superposition in optical image formation.

It is in this spirit then that we now propose the notion that an optical image can be considered as a linear superposition of impulse (point source) responses integrated over the entire object plane. In Fig. 1–6, we make the simplifying assumptions that the magnification is unity; that the light is incoherent so that the intensity adds linearly; that the distribution of light at (x', y'), due to a point source of light at (x, y), is given by $g(x' - x, y' - y)$ and that this distribution does not change as we explore the field. Then, if $o(x, y)$ describes the brightness of the object, and $i(x', y')$ the brightness in the image, we have

$$i(x', y') = \int\limits_{-\infty}^{+\infty}\!\!\int g(x' - x, y' - y)o(x, y) \, dx \, dy, \qquad (1\text{–}16)$$

where the actual limits on the size of the object have been absorbed into $o(x, y)$. In other words, Eq. (1–16) states that each point in the object

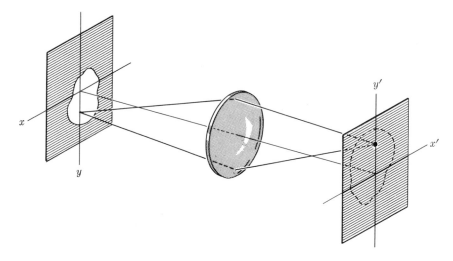

FIGURE 1–6

plane radiates independently of every other point and produces a point image whose strength and position is determined by $o(x, y)\, dx\, dy$. The final image is a weighted sum of these impulse responses integrated over the object plane.

The purpose of the remainder of this book is to examine in detail how one can apply the concepts of filter theory, expressed in Eq. (1–16) and developed for the most part in electrical communication theory, to the theory of optical image formation. In short, from this point on, we will continue to consider image forming optical systems as filters of spatial frequencies.

REFERENCES

1. E. L. INCE, *Ordinary Differential Equations.* Dover (1953).

2. H. MARGENAU and G. M. MURPHY, *The Mathematics of Physics and Chemistry.* D. Van Nostrand (1956).

3. P. M. MORSE and H. FESHBACK, *Methods of Theoretical Physics.* Vol. 1. McGraw-Hill (1953).

4. E. J. BAGHDADY, *Lectures on Communication Systems Theory.* McGraw-Hill (1961).

2

Spatial versus Time Filters

We saw in Chapter 1 that as a direct consequence of describing fields and physical devices in terms of linear differential operators there results a principle of linear superposition. In addition, we saw that the weighting factor which allows us to perform this superposition over the source to find the response is just the Green's function or impulse response. Finally, we recall that it was not sufficient to state that $g(x, x')$ must satisfy the differential equation, but one must in addition specify the boundary conditions imposed on $g(x, x')$.

Since this approach is so common in various fields of physics and engineering, it is no surprise to find that one can describe the formation of an optical image in terms of a weighted integral over the object plane, the weighting function being the distribution of light in the image of a point source. This notion is so conceptually satisfying that it is tempting to carry over directly all the techniques that have been developed over the years in electric circuitry and bring them to bear on problems of image formation in optical systems. There is a danger, however, in proceeding blindly in this fashion. Spatial filters have inherent properties which make them essentially different from time filters. For the most part, we shall confine our attention to optical systems linear in the time averaged square of the electric vector, which is the light intensity. Nevertheless, much of what we say will be applicable (with some modifications) to infrared, and TV and radio antenna scanning systems. Later, with suitable constraints, we shall examine the properties of optical systems linear in complex amplitude; that is, systems for which the illumination is said to be coherent. For the present, however, we restrict the discussion to somewhat ideal optical systems for which the illumination is incoherent, the magnification is unity, and for which the distribution of light in the point image does not change as one explores the working field of the instrument. The extent to which these restrictions can be relaxed will be examined later. However, we now wish to compare the behavior of time with space filters.

12

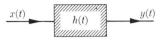

FIGURE 2–1

2–1 Time filters

Consider the system shown in Fig. 2–1. We now label the impulse response of the device $h(t)$, and we characterize the linear operation by which $x(t)$ produces $y(t)$ by the equation

$$Lx(t) = y(t). \qquad (2\text{–}1)$$

Let us now confine our attention to time filters that satisfy the following conditions.

(a) *Linearity.*

$$L[ax_1(t) + bx_2(t)] = ay_1(t) + by_2(t);$$

that is, adding two inputs results in adding their outputs, and doubling one input, for example, doubles the other.

(b) *Invariance.*

$$L[x(t + t')] = y(t + t').$$

The form of the output is insensitive to a translation of the time axis. These two conditions are sufficient, so far, to establish e^{st} as an eigenfunction of the operator L, where t is the real time variable, but where s, in general, can be complex.

(c) *Causality.*

$$h(t) = 0, \qquad t < 0.$$

One must exclude anticipative effects. In other words, there can be no response until one closes the switch. In terms of the convolution or folding integral, this implies that standing at some point in time, one can look into the past but not into the future.

(d) *Stability.*

$$\int_{-\infty}^{+\infty} |h(t)| \, dt < \infty.$$

Every bounded input yields a bounded output. The fact that the system is passive (no active elements, batteries, generators, etc.) when translated into mathematical language demands that the impulse response be absolutely integrable.

The first two requirements lead directly to the superposition integral

$$y(t) = \int_{-\infty}^{+\infty} h(t - t')x(t') \, dt'. \qquad (2\text{–}2)$$

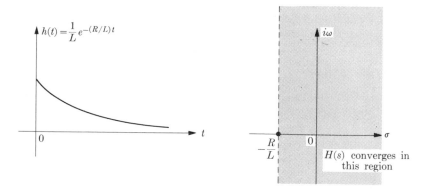

FIGURE 2–2

To examine the last two requirements, however, it becomes necessary to generalize the Fourier transform and consider the complex frequency $s = \sigma + i\omega$. Taking the Laplace transform of Eq. (2–1) yields

$$H(s) = \frac{Y(s)}{X(s)} = \int_{-\infty}^{+\infty} h(t)e^{-st}\, dt, \qquad (2\text{--}3)$$

where, conversely,

$$h(t) = \frac{1}{2\pi i} \int_{\sigma_0 - i\infty}^{\sigma_0 + i\infty} H(s)e^{st}\, ds.$$

It is absolutely essential to understand that $H(s)$ lies in the strip of the s-plane for which $H(s)$ is defined, and that outside this strip, $H(s)$ does not exist. The width and location of this strip in the s-plane, as we shall see, are determined from the completely *separate* physical requirements (c) and (d) above. For example, consider the $R\text{-}L$ circuit discussed in Chapter 1. By any one of several physical arguments, we can show that

$$h(t) = \frac{1}{L}e^{-(R/L)t}, \qquad t \geq 0.$$

For this case, Eq. (2–3) becomes

$$H(s) = \int_0^\infty h(t)e^{-st}\, dt = \frac{1}{R + Ls}[1 - \lim_{t \to \infty} e^{-[(R/L)+s]\,t}],$$

so that

$$H(s) = \frac{1}{R + Ls} \quad \text{if and only if} \quad \sigma > -\frac{R}{L},$$

where $s = \sigma + i\omega$. (See Fig. 2–2.)

Let us now list the conditions that $H(s)$ must satisfy in the complex frequency plane as a result of the requirements (a) through (d) above.

(1) Since

$$H(i\omega) = \int_0^\infty e^{-i\omega t} h(t) \, dt,$$

$$|H(i\omega)| \leq \int_0^\infty |e^{i\omega t}| \, |h(t)| \, dt = \int_0^\infty |h(t)| \, dt$$

so that the stability requirement implies that the transform exists on the $i\omega$-axis, and is bounded there.

(2) If $h(t)$ is real, $H(s^*) = H^*(s)$.

(3) The causality condition implies that the real and imaginary parts of $H(i\omega)$ are related by a Hilbert transform [1].

(4) All poles of $H(s)$ are located in the left half plane.

The last is a result of the two separate conditions of causality and stability mentioned above. The causality condition demands that the domain of convergence of $H(s)$ be at least a right half plane. The stability condition demands that the domain of convergence of $H(s)$ include at least the imaginary axis $s = i\omega$. When *both* conditions are imposed we can do no better than quote Siebert [2]: "However, if a system is both stable and realizable, then the domain of convergence of $H(s)$ is at least the entire right half-plane $Re[s] > 0$. But unless realizability is implied, the statement that 'an unstable system is one whose system function has a singularity in the right half-plane' is an oversimplification."

The choice of a path of integration in the complex s-plane is intimately associated with the earlier statements concerning the boundary conditions on the Green's function. In the same way that g is not unique unless the boundary conditions are specified, $H(s)$ and hence $h(t)$ is not unique unless the domain of convergence is specified as Siebert has so graphically demonstrated (see Fig. 2–3). By keeping the poles on the left as we proceed up the imaginary axis, Jordan's lemma and the theory of residues insures that $h(t) = 0, t < 0$ for the infinite semicircle enveloping the right half plane. The form of $h(t)$ for $t > 0$ is determined by the poles enclosed by the infinite path encircling the left half plane.

2–2 Classification of input signals

Let us turn now to a description of the signals entering the time filter under discussion. In general, we can characterize $x(t)$ as a periodic, transient, or random waveform. In all three cases, the superposition integral of Eq. (2–2) is valid since it is based on conditions (a) and (b). The imposition of the other conditions merely demands that we integrate only

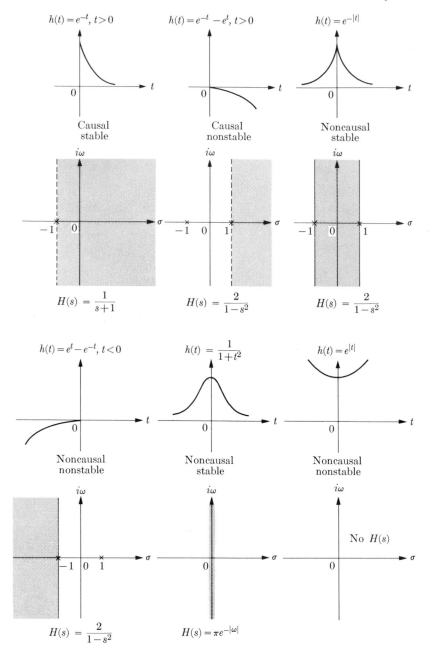

FIG. 2–3. [From E. J. Baghdady, *Lectures on Communication Systems Theory,* New York: McGraw-Hill Book Co. (1961).]

from the infinite past up to the present t, but not into the future. Further, $h(t - t')$ represents a folded form of $h(t')$ looking into the past. In frequency space, the simple multiplicative relation,

$$Y(\omega) = H(\omega)X(\omega),$$

remains valid for periodic and transient inputs, where X and Y represent Fourier coefficients and Fourier transforms, respectively. For random waveforms over an infinite interval, the Fourier transform does not exist, and one is forced to resort to a statistical description.

2–3 Random signals

It is here that the concepts of correlation functions and power density spectra become useful. Although it is not possible to specify what happens to any one waveform in frequency space, it is possible to preserve a multiplicative relation between the input and output in terms of a time averaged density function which describes the amount of power between ω and $\omega + d\omega$. Because of the statistical nature of this description, we cannot expect to maintain phase information since there will exist whole classes of functions obeying the same statistics and hence possessing the same power density spectrum. Since these notions are so well known [3] in the field of electrical communication theory, we make no attempt to derive them here, but rather list the most important relations.

Starting with $x(t)$, a random waveform, we define its autocorrelation $\phi_{xx}(\tau)$ as

$$\phi_{xx}(\tau) = \langle x(t)x(t + \tau)\rangle = \lim_{T \to \infty} \frac{1}{2T} \int_{-T}^{+T} x(t)x(t + \tau)\, dt.$$

This function possesses the following properties:

$$\text{(a)} \quad \phi_{xx}(0) = \langle x^2 \rangle$$

represents the total power in the waveform.

$$\text{(b)} \quad \phi_{xx}(\tau) = \phi_{xx}(-\tau)$$

is an even function of τ.

$$\text{(c)} \quad \phi_{xx}(0) > |\phi_{xx}(\tau)|.$$

$$\text{(d)} \quad \phi_{xx}(\infty) = \langle x \rangle^2$$

represents the d-c power in the waveform. Therefore $\phi_{xx}(0) - \phi_{xx}(\infty)$ represents the a-c power (Fig. 2–4).

If the random process is stationary (statistics do not change with time), then this time average will agree with the average taken over an ensemble

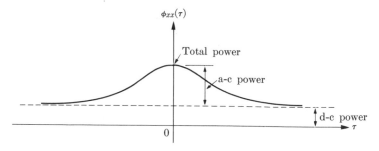

FIGURE 2–4

of similarly prepared random functions. That is,

$$\phi_{xx}(\tau) = \langle x(t)x(t + \tau)\rangle = \iint\limits_{-\infty}^{+\infty} x_1 x_2 w_\tau(x_1, x_2) \, dx_1 \, dx_2,$$

where $w_\tau(x_1, x_2) \, dx_1 \, dx_2$ represents the probability that x_1 lies between x_1 and $x_1 + dx_1$, *and* that x_2 lies between x_2 and $x_2 + dx_2$, when separated by a time τ. Similar definitions can be given for the output waveform $y(t)$. It is characteristic of the Gaussian distribution that if the input of a *linear* device is so distributed, so will the output. The equivalent statistical description of the random function $x(t)$ in the frequency domain is provided by the Wiener-Khinchin theorem

$$\Phi_{xx}(\omega) = \int_{-\infty}^{+\infty} \phi_{xx}(\tau)e^{-i\omega\tau} \, d\tau,$$

where $\Phi_{xx}(\omega)$ is the power density spectrum of $x(t)$, so named from the relation

$$\Phi_{xx}(\omega) = \lim_{T\to\infty} \frac{|X_T(\omega)|^2}{2T},$$

where $X_T(\omega)$ is the Fourier transform of a sample of $x(t)$ taken over the interval $(-T, T)$. From the properties of $\phi_{xx}(\tau)$, $\Phi_{xx}(\omega)$ is a real, even positive function of ω. In short, $\Phi_{xx}(\omega)$ and $\phi_{xx}(\tau)$ are said to be Fourier cosine transform pairs.

It is clear that one can define similar statistical descriptions of the output waveform $y(t)$. The question is, how are these descriptions $\phi_{yy}(\tau)$ and $\Phi_{yy}(\omega)$ related to $\phi_{xx}(\tau)$ and $\Phi_{xx}(\omega)$? Let us start with the definition of $\phi_{yy}(\tau)$; that is,

$$\phi_{yy}(\tau) = \langle y(t)y(t + \tau)\rangle.$$

Substituting for $y(t)$ and $y(t + \tau)$, two superposition integrals of the form of Eq. 2–2, we get

$$\phi_{yy}(\tau) = \int_{-\infty}^{+\infty} \phi_{hh}(t - \tau)\phi_{xx}(t) \, dt,$$

where

$$\phi_{hh}(t - \tau) = \int_{-\infty}^{+\infty} h(t - \tau + \sigma)h(\sigma) \, d\sigma \qquad (2\text{–}4)$$

Replacing the integral in Eq. (2–4) by the Fourier transform of the product of the transforms of $\phi_{hh}(\tau)$ and $\phi_{xx}(\tau)$, we have

$$\phi_{yy}(\tau) = \frac{1}{2\pi} \int_{-\infty}^{+\infty} |H(\omega)|^2 \Phi_{xx}(\omega)e^{i\omega\tau} \, d\omega, \qquad (2\text{–}5)$$

and since $\phi_{yy}(\tau)$ and $\Phi_{yy}(\omega)$ are Fourier transform pairs,

$$\Phi_{yy}(\omega) = |H(\omega)|^2 \Phi_{xx}(\omega).$$

Thus, although phase information has been lost, we have been able to preserve the multiplication relation in frequency space. As a result, if we had a number n of systems in cascade, such that the output of one served as the input to the next, Eqs. (2–5) and (2–2) remain valid with the understanding that

$$H(\omega) = \prod_{i=1}^{n} H_i(\omega). \qquad (2\text{–}6)$$

This is a good example of the axiom that a chain is as strong as its weakest link. The simple form of Eq. (2–6) is to be compared with an equivalent n-fold convolution in the time domain representing the equivalent impulse response $h(t)$.

Often one is interested in the extent of the mean square fluctuations at the output of a linear filter, and this is given in Eqs. (2–4) and (2–5) by setting $\tau = 0$, since

$$\phi_{yy}(0) = \langle y^2(t) \rangle,$$

$$\langle y^2 \rangle = \int_{-\infty}^{+\infty} \phi_{hh}(t)\phi_{xx}(t) \, dt$$

$$= \frac{1}{2\pi} \int_{-\infty}^{+\infty} |H(\omega)|^2 \Phi_{xx}(\omega) \, d\omega.$$

Note that if one wishes to assess the system on the basis of $\langle y^2 \rangle$, the fact that $H(\omega)$ enters as $|H(\omega)|$ does not allow one to infer the extent to which the peaks and troughs of the output waveform $y(t)$ are correlated with the peaks and troughs of the input waveform $x(t)$. To this end we now form the cross correlation between the input and output waveforms defined as

$$\phi_{xy}(\tau) = \langle x(t)y(t + \tau)\rangle.$$

Once again we replace $y(t + \tau)$ by the equivalent superposition integral in Eq. (2–2), and a little manipulation [3] results in the interesting relation

$$\phi_{xy}(\tau) = \int_{-\infty}^{+\infty} h(\tau + t)\phi_{xx}(t)\, dt. \qquad (2\text{–}7)$$

Again taking the Fourier transform of both sides, we have

$$\Phi_{xy}(\omega) = H(\omega)\Phi_{xx}(\omega), \qquad (2\text{–}8)$$

where the phase information in $H(\omega)$ now remains. In fact we can define a measure of the resemblance between $x(t)$ and $y(t)$ by again setting $\tau = 0$ in Eqs. (2–7) and (2–8) and getting

$$\langle x(t)y(t)\rangle = \phi_{xy}(0) = \int_{-\infty}^{+\infty} h(t)\phi_{xx}(t)\, dt$$

$$= \int_{-\infty}^{+\infty} H(\omega)\Phi_{xx}(\omega)\, d\omega.$$

Finally we can define still a third quantity, the average mean-squared difference between the input and output of the system

$$E = \langle [y(t) - x(t)]^2\rangle,$$

which will clearly include both factors just discussed. This in fact was the starting point of Wiener's approach to optimum filtering.

2–4 Optical spatial filters

Consider the simple optical system shown in Fig. 2–5. To avoid unduly complicated notation later, we now define the following terms:

$o(\xi, \eta) \equiv$ the light intensity distribution over the object plane.

$i(x, y) \equiv$ the light intensity distribution over the image plane.

$s(x - \xi, y - \eta) \equiv$ the "spread function" describing the distribution of light at (x, y) due to a point source at (ξ, η).

Further, these functions have two dimensional spectral distributions described by

$$I(\omega) = I(\omega_x, \omega_y) = \iint_{-\infty}^{+\infty} i(x, y)e^{-i\boldsymbol{\omega}\cdot\mathbf{r}}\, dx\, dy,$$

where

$$\boldsymbol{\omega} \cdot \mathbf{r} = \omega_x x + \omega_y y,$$

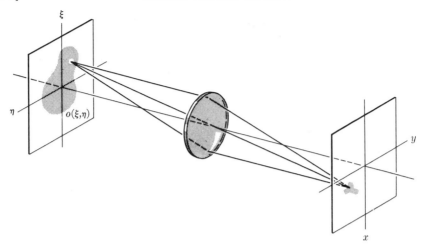

FIGURE 2–5

with a similar expression existing for $0(\omega)$. Next, unless otherwise stated, the Fourier transform of $s(x, y)$ will be normalized to unity at $\omega_x = \omega_y = 0$ and will be labeled the optical transfer function $\tau(\omega)$ or the frequency response, thus:

$$\tau(\omega) = \frac{\displaystyle\iint_{-\infty}^{+\infty} s(x, y)e^{-i\omega \cdot \mathbf{r}}\, dx\, dy}{\displaystyle\iint_{-\infty}^{+\infty} s(x, y)\, dx\, dy}.$$

Let us now turn our attention to the four conditions (a) through (d) in the previous section. Clearly the causality condition (c) is a direct consequence of the fact that the independent variable t represents time. In optical systems, the light distribution not only exists on both sides* of the coordinate axes but often it possesses symmetry. Therefore the causality condition can, in general, be relaxed in optics. The invariance condition (b) is another matter, however [4]. The light distribution in the point image does not remain the same as one explores the working field of the instrument. We will, in fact, examine, in the next chapter, the dependence of the aberration coefficients on the field angle. In an attempt to preserve the optical-electrical analogy, we now are forced to appeal to the fact that

---

* An interesting optical example where this is not true lies in the Foucault knife-edge test where one half or more of the Fraunhofer spectrum is abruptly chopped off. As Linfoot [5] has shown, this leads directly to the introduction of Hilbert transforms.

this light distribution, in practice, does not change abruptly as one moves away from the optical axis. As a consequence, we shall agree to employ the invariance condition with the understanding that the image plane has been decomposed into zones over which the spread function does not change appreciably. In practice then, it will become necessary in representing the transfer function $\tau(\omega)$, graphically, to include separate plots as a function of field angle, focal position, and wavelength (color).

With this simplifying assumption, we now state that since each element in the object plane $o(\xi, \eta) \, d\xi \, d\eta$ produces a patch of light

$$o(\xi, \eta) s(x - \xi, y - \eta) \, d\xi \, d\eta$$

at the point (x, y) then the image distribution, due to all elements over the object plane, is given by

$$i(x, y) = \int\limits_{-\infty}^{+\infty} \!\!\! \int s(x - \xi, y - \eta) o(\xi, \eta) \, d\xi \, d\eta. \tag{2-9}$$

Taking the Fourier transform of both sides, we get the equation

$$I(\omega) = \tau(\omega) O(\omega),$$

where $\tau(\omega)$, in general, is a normalized, complex function of the two-dimensional space-frequency variables ω_x and ω_y whose dimensions are in radians per length.

2–5 The optical contrast transfer function

Often, it is convenient to test optical systems by using line charts which vary along one dimension only. In such cases, one can define the one-dimensional impulse response or line-spread function $l(x)$ by using Eq. (2–9) for an object consisting of an infinitely thin line source $o(\xi, \eta) = \delta(\xi)$:

$$l(x) = \int\limits_{-\infty}^{+\infty} \!\!\! \int s(x - \xi, y - \eta) \, \delta(\xi) \, d\xi \, d\eta = \int_{-\infty}^{+\infty} s(x, y - \eta) \, d(y - \eta).$$

In reducing the problem to a one-dimensional variation, we should not get the impression that the frequency response becomes one dimensional. In general, the spread function $s(x, y)$ is not rotationally symmetric, so line structures oriented differently in the object plane will be imaged with varying degrees of contrast. For a line structure oriented at an angle θ with the x-axis, for example, a simple rotation will cause the new coordinate system (x', y') to align itself along and perpendicular to the line structure. It must then be understood that the line-spread function should be written as $l(x, \theta)$ and its Fourier transform, the transfer function, as $\tau(\omega, \theta)$.

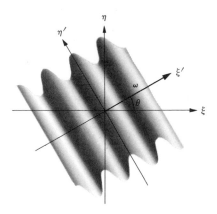

FIGURE 2–6

Complete information is obtained then, by determining $\tau(\omega, \theta)$ for all angles θ. Finally, in those cases for which rotational symmetry does exist, the two-dimensional Fourier transformations, as shown in Appendix B, reduce to Fourier-Bessel transforms.

To illustrate these notions, consider a sinusoidal test chart in the object plane whose background brightness is B_0 and whose modulation is B_1. Further, let the wave vector ω make an angle θ with the ξ-axis (see Fig. 2–6). In terms of the spatial period p in mm, $\omega = 2\pi/p$, and we can write

$$o(\xi, \eta) = B_0 + B_1 \cos \omega \xi' = B_0(1 + C_0 \cos \omega \xi'),$$

where $C_0 = B_1/B_0$ is the object contrast, and where the primed and unprimed coordinates are related through the matrix which describes the rotation in the form

$$\begin{pmatrix} \xi' \\ \eta' \end{pmatrix} = \begin{pmatrix} \cos \theta & \sin \theta \\ -\sin \theta & \cos \theta \end{pmatrix} \begin{pmatrix} \xi \\ \eta \end{pmatrix}.$$

To keep in mind that the object and image coordinates have been rotated to align ξ' and x' with the wave vector ω, we include θ as a parameter in the superposition integral of Eq. (2–9),

$$i(x', \theta) = \iint s(x' - \xi', y' - \eta')(B_0 + B_1 \cos \omega \xi') \, d\xi' \, d\eta'.$$

Performing the integration over η', we get

$$i(x', \theta) = B_0 \int_{-\infty}^{+\infty} l(x' - \xi', \theta) \, d\xi' + B_1 \int_{-\infty}^{+\infty} l(x' - \xi', \theta) \cos \omega \xi' \, d\xi'.$$

The first integral is merely a constant $\tau(0)$ representing the total illumination in the spread function. The second integral can be expanded with a change of variable $\sigma = x' - \xi'$ into the form

$$\frac{\int_{-\infty}^{+\infty} l(\sigma) \cos \omega(x' - \sigma)\, d\sigma}{\int_{-\infty}^{+\infty} l(\sigma)\, d\sigma} = \tau_c(\omega) \cos \omega x' + \tau_s(\omega) \sin \omega x',$$

where τ_c and τ_s are the normalized cosine and sine transforms of the impulse response, respectively:

$$\tau_c(\omega) = \frac{\int_{-\infty}^{+\infty} l(\sigma) \cos \omega \sigma\, d\sigma}{\int_{-\infty}^{+\infty} l(\sigma)\, d\sigma}, \qquad \tau_s(\omega) = \frac{\int_{-\infty}^{+\infty} l(\sigma) \sin \omega \sigma\, d\sigma}{\int_{-\infty}^{+\infty} l(\sigma)\, d\sigma}.$$

We see that the light distribution in the image (Fig. 2–7) can be written as

$$i(x', \theta) = B_0'[1 + C_i(\omega) \cos \{\omega x' - \phi(\omega)\}],$$

where

$$B_0' = \tau(o)B_0,$$

$$|\tau(\omega)| = \frac{C_i}{C_o} = \sqrt{\tau_c^2 + \tau_s^2},$$

$$\phi(\omega) = \tan^{-1} \frac{\tau_s}{\tau_c}.$$

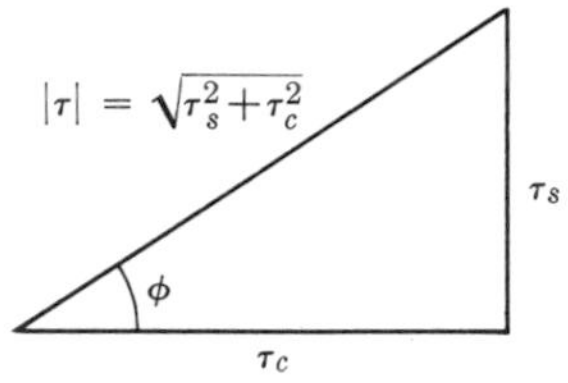

$|\tau| = \sqrt{\tau_s^2 + \tau_c^2}$

τ_s

ϕ

τ_c

FIGURE 2–7

Thus we see that a sine wave will always be imaged as a sine wave with, at most, its amplitude and phase altered (Fig. 2–8). We also see the reason for labeling $\tau(\omega)$ as the optical-contrast transfer function. If the object had consisted of black and white bars, then by Fourier decomposition, we could treat each component being imaged separately so that it yields

$$i(x', \theta) = B_0' \left\{ 1 + \frac{4}{\pi} \sum_{n=0}^{\infty} \frac{(-1)^n |\tau(\omega_n)|}{2n + 1} \cos\left[(2n + 1)\omega x' - \phi(\omega_n)\right] \right\}.$$

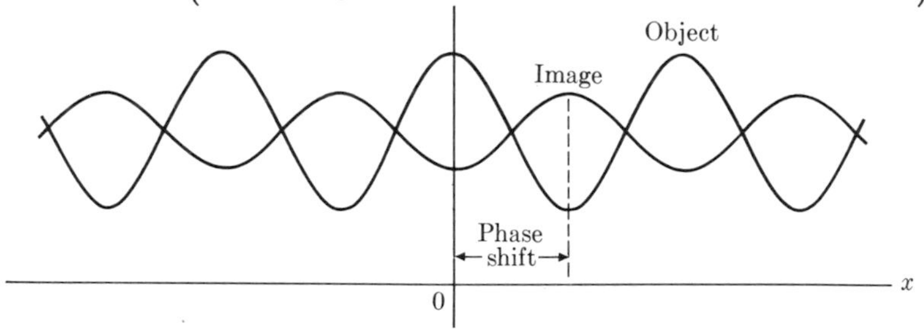

FIGURE 2–8

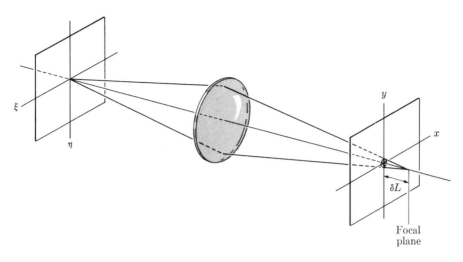

FIGURE 2–9

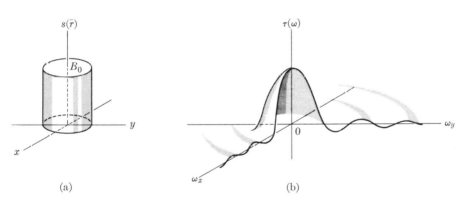

(a) (b)

FIGURE 2–10

2–6 An idealized illustration

As another example to illustrate the way in which one can consider optical systems as filters of spatial frequencies, we now treat a problem in image formation from a very elementary point of view. Consider what happens to a perfect optical image (Fig. 2–9) as we move out of focus. Here, by perfect, we mean that the effects of diffraction and aberrations are to be ignored. Later we shall examine these effects on the structure of the image, but for the time being, we make this idealization to illustrate a point.

Assuming then that the spread function or impulse response for this case is the pillbox distribution shown in Fig. 2–10(a), we have, for the frequency

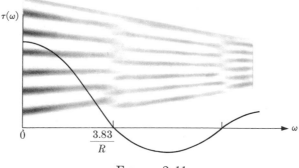

$$\text{FIGURE 2–11}$$

response,

$$\tau(\omega) = \frac{\int_0^R B_0 J_0(\omega r) r \, dr}{\int_0^R B_0 r \, dr}, \tag{2–10}$$

where, from the inherent rotational symmetry, we use the Fourier-Bessel transform. Making use of the well-known relation for Bessel functions,

$$\frac{d}{dz}[z^n J_n(z)] = z^n J_{n-1}(z)$$

for $n = 1$, Eq. (2–10) reduces to

$$\tau(\omega) = 2\frac{J_1(\omega R)}{\omega R},$$

as shown in Fig. 2–10(b). The first resolution limit occurs at $J_1(3.83) = 0$ or in terms of $\omega = 2\pi/p = 3.83/R$. Thus, for a ratio of spot diameter to period of a sinusoidal chart given by $2R/p = 1.22$, no contrast will be seen in the image. For a higher-frequency line chart, $\tau(\omega)$ becomes negative indicating 180° phase shift in space. That is, the black and white lines have interchanged their positions. This process of passing through zero contrast to abrupt phase shifts proceeds along the lines shown in Fig. 2–10(b). This effect, known in optics as "spurious resolution," can be dramatically demonstrated by projecting a series of converging bars on a screen and throwing the projector out of focus. One can readily see the zero contrast bands move across the chart together with the abrupt phase shifts, as shown in Fig. 2–11.

One can of course obtain the shape of this curve merely by visualizing what happens in the convolution integral, as the spot scans the chart. First, when the spot is much smaller than the spacing between lines, it merely rounds off the edges. Later, when the diameter of the spot is of the order of magnitude of the spacing, one will gain light at the same rate as one loses light in the scanning process and hence detect no change (zero contrast). Further, in the scanning process, when the scanning spot includes two lines, it will actually pick up more light from bright bands on either side when it is centered on a black line and vice versa; this accounts for the spurious region. Thus the process proceeds in this fashion. Hence, although the problem has been formulated for the ideal case of a lens out of focus, the approach and analysis can often be applied to other (for example TV and infrared) scanning systems for which the spread functions may approximate the pillbox distribution shown in Fig. 2–10(a).

2–7 Image motion

As a final example of the use of these methods for elementary situations in optics, and before proceeding to a detailed description of how one determines the frequency response of real optical systems, we now proceed to demonstrate how we can take into account the effect of relative motion between the object and image planes. More precisely, the problem is this: given $s(\mathbf{r})$ and $\tau(\omega)$ both rotationally symmetric, how does one determine $s'(x, y)$ and $\tau'(\omega)$ when relative motion of uniform velocity v causes each point to be smeared out a length $L = vt$ along, say, the x-direction? So far as the new point image $s'(x, y)$ is concerned, we can write

$$s'(x, y) = \int_{-L/2}^{L/2} s(x - \xi, y) \, d\xi; \qquad (2\text{–}11)$$

that is, $s'(x, y)$ can be regarded as the image produced by the undisturbed system $s(x, y)$ when viewing a thin bright line of length L along the ξ-axis, as shown in Fig. 2–12, where $R(\xi)$ represents the rectangular function. Thus we can consider Eq. (2–11) as a superposition integral over the object plane in the form

$$s'(x, y) = \int\!\!\!\int_{-\infty}^{+\infty} s(x - \xi; y - \eta) R(\xi) \, \delta(\eta) \, d\xi \, d\eta.$$

To determine $\tau'(\omega)$, we take the Fourier transform of both sides and, in the process, invoke the convolution theorem for the transform of a product, so that

$$\tau'(\omega) = \tau(\omega) \left(\frac{\sin (\omega_x L)/2}{(\omega_x L)/2} \right).$$

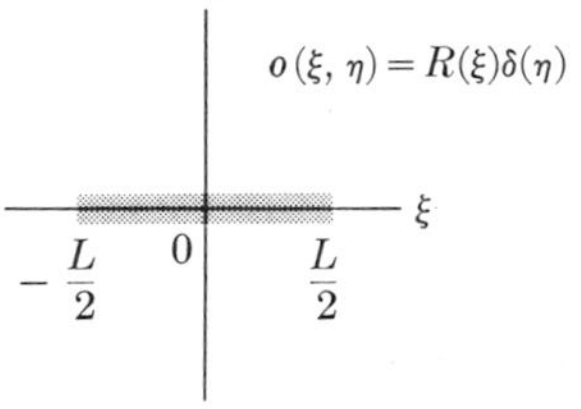

Thus, with motion, we can consider the effective frequency response as the result of two static systems in cascade; the first produces $\tau(\omega)$, and

$o(\xi, \eta) = R(\xi)\delta(\eta)$

FIGURE 2–12

$$\text{TABLE 2-1}$$

	Time filters	Space filters
Superposition integral	$y(t) = \displaystyle\int_{-\infty}^{t} h(t - t')x(t')\,dt'$	$i(x, y) = \displaystyle\iint_{-\infty}^{+\infty} s(\mathbf{x} - \boldsymbol{\xi})o(\boldsymbol{\xi})\,d\boldsymbol{\xi}$
Periodic input	$x(t) = \displaystyle\sum_{-\infty}^{+\infty} X_n e^{i\omega_n t}$ $y(t) = \displaystyle\sum_{-\infty}^{+\infty} Y_n e^{i\omega_n t}$ $Y_n = H(\omega_n)X_n$	$o(\xi, \eta) = \displaystyle\sum_{m,n=-\infty}^{+\infty} O_{mn} e^{i\boldsymbol{\rho}\cdot\boldsymbol{\omega}_{mn}}$ $i(x, y) = \displaystyle\sum_{m,n=-\infty}^{+\infty} I_{mn} e^{i\mathbf{r}\cdot\boldsymbol{\omega}_{mn}}$ $I_{mn} = \tau(\boldsymbol{\omega}_{m,n})O_{mn}$
Transient input	$x(t) = \dfrac{1}{2\pi}\displaystyle\int_{-\infty}^{+\infty} X(\omega)e^{i\omega t}\,d\omega$ $y(t) = \dfrac{1}{2\pi}\displaystyle\int_{-\infty}^{+\infty} Y(\omega)e^{i\omega t}\,d\omega$ $Y(\omega) = H(\omega)X(\omega)$	$o(\boldsymbol{\rho}) = \dfrac{1}{(2\pi)^2}\displaystyle\iint_{-\infty}^{+\infty} O(\boldsymbol{\omega})e^{i\boldsymbol{\omega}\cdot\boldsymbol{\rho}}\,d\boldsymbol{\omega}$ $i(\mathbf{r}) = \dfrac{1}{(2\pi)^2}\displaystyle\iint_{-\infty}^{+\infty} I(\boldsymbol{\omega})e^{i\boldsymbol{\omega}\cdot\mathbf{r}}\,d\boldsymbol{\omega}$ $I(\boldsymbol{\omega}) = \tau(\boldsymbol{\omega})O(\boldsymbol{\omega})$
Random input	$\phi_{xx}(\boldsymbol{\tau}) = \langle x(t)x(t + \tau)\rangle$ $\phi_{yy}(\boldsymbol{\tau}) = \langle y(t)y(t + \tau)\rangle$ $\Phi(\omega) = \displaystyle\int_{-\infty}^{+\infty} \phi(\tau)\cos\omega\tau\,d\tau$ $\phi_{yy}(\tau) = \displaystyle\int_{-\infty}^{+\infty} \phi_{hh}(t - \tau)\phi_{xx}(t)dt$ $\Phi_{yy}(\omega) = |H(\omega)|^2\Phi_{xx}(\omega)$ $\phi_{xy}(\tau) = \displaystyle\int_{-\infty}^{+\infty} h(\tau + t)\phi_{xx}(t)\,dt$ $\Phi_{xy}(\omega) = \Phi_{xx}(\omega)H(\omega)$	$\phi_{oo}(\boldsymbol{\rho}') = \langle o(\boldsymbol{\rho})o(\boldsymbol{\rho} + \boldsymbol{\rho}')\rangle^{*}$ $\phi_{ii}(\boldsymbol{\rho}') = \langle i(\boldsymbol{\rho})i(\boldsymbol{\rho} + \boldsymbol{\rho}')\rangle$ $\Phi(\boldsymbol{\omega}) = \displaystyle\iint_{-\infty}^{+\infty} \phi(\mathbf{r})e^{-i(\boldsymbol{\omega}\cdot\mathbf{r})}\,d\mathbf{r}$ $\phi_{ii}(\mathbf{r}) = \displaystyle\iint_{-\infty}^{+\infty} \phi_{ss}(\boldsymbol{\rho} - \mathbf{r})\phi_{oo}(\boldsymbol{\rho})\,d\boldsymbol{\rho}$ $\Phi_{ii}(\boldsymbol{\omega}) = |\tau(\boldsymbol{\omega})|^2\Phi_{oo}(\boldsymbol{\omega})$ $\phi_{io}(\mathbf{r}) = \displaystyle\iint_{-\infty}^{+\infty} s(\mathbf{r} + \boldsymbol{\rho})\phi_{oo}(\boldsymbol{\rho})\,d\boldsymbol{\rho}$ $\Phi_{io}(\boldsymbol{\omega}) = \tau(\boldsymbol{\omega})\Phi_{oo}(\boldsymbol{\omega})$

* The space average, $\langle f \rangle$ is defined by $\quad \langle f \rangle = \displaystyle\lim_{L\to\infty} \dfrac{1}{4L^2}\int_{-L}^{+L}\int_{-L}^{+L} f(\boldsymbol{\rho})\,d\boldsymbol{\rho}.$

the second produces a maximum effect on line structures whose normal points along the direction of motion and has no effect on line structure at a right angle to the motion. The effect on other orientations can be determined by setting $\omega_x = \omega \cos \theta$.

In closing this chapter, we use the analog between optical and electrical filters, once more, to state that we can consider all brightness distributions in object space to be periodic, transient, or random; and all the relations previously discussed for time filters will hold in optics with minor alterations.

First the transform relations are, of course, two dimensional. Second, for incoherent illumination it is the light intensity which adds linearly so that all inputs and outputs are everywhere positive functions. In many cases, we are interested in fluctuations about the mean brightness, and these representations, of course, can be both positive and negative. Finally, the averages for the correlation functions and their transforms are space and not time averages over a large area. As a result, "power" density spectrum is not an appropriate term to use, and we choose instead the term Wiener spectrum to represent the Fourier transform of a correlation function. Otherwise everything is analogous and we summarize the transitions in Table 2–1.*

REFERENCES

1. E. A. GUILLEMIN, *Synthesis of Passive Networks.* Wiley (1957).

2. E. J. BAGHDADY, *Lectures on Communication Systems Theory.* McGraw-Hill (1961).

3. Y. W. LEE, *Statistical Theory of Communication.* Wiley (1960).

4. P. DUMONTET, *Optica Acta* **2,** 53 (1955).

5. E. H. LINFOOT, *Recent Advances in Optics.* Oxford Univ. Press (1955).

6. A. PAPOULIS, *The Fourier Integral and its Applications.* McGraw-Hill (1962).

7. A. MARÉCHAL and M. FRANÇON, *Editions de la Revue d'Optique.* Paris (1960).

---

* It is an unfortunate accident of terminology that the subscripts i and o for image and object in optics have just the opposite significance in time filters when signifying input (i) and output (o) waveforms.

3

Introduction to Geometrical Optics

3–1 Fermat's principle and Snell's law of refraction

It is common practice in physics to describe fields in terms of variational principles. Perhaps the oldest variational principle in physics is Fermat's principle governing geometrical optics. It states, that a ray of light will traverse a medium in such a way that the total optical path (the index of refraction μ times the geometrical length) assumes an extreme value. That is, the ray will proceed from P_1 to P_2 in such a way that[*]

$$\delta L = \delta \int_{P_1}^{P_2} \mu \, ds = 0. \tag{3–1}$$

We should not jump at teleological implications here. Often the path is a maximum, not a minimum. Fermat's principle merely indicates an extremum. For a homogeneous medium ($\mu =$ const), the Euler-Lagrange differential equation associated with Eq. (3–1) results in straight line (rectilinear) propagation. For an inhomogeneous medium (for example, through the atmosphere with its varying density and hence index of refraction) the path which satisfies Eq. (3–1) describes the point by point bending of the ray.

Let us apply Fermat's principle to the problem of refraction at a surface separating two homogeneous media having indices of refraction μ and μ'. (See Fig. 3–1.) In this figure and throughout the section, we shall confine our attention to rays in the xz-plane and let ϕ and ϕ' indicate the angles that the incident and refracted rays make with the normal PC to the surface. For this case, Fermat's principle reduces to

$$\delta L = \mu(s + \delta s) + \mu'(s' + \delta s') - (\mu s + \mu' s') = 0,$$

or

$$\mu \, \delta s + \mu' \, \delta s' = 0,$$

_____

[*] Since $\mu = c/v$, this principle often appears as a stationary integral over time $\delta \int c \, dt = 0$.

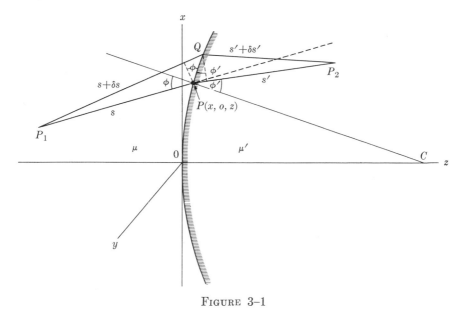

FIGURE 3–1

where δ indicates a small variation about the actual path. From the geometry, we see that

$$s + \delta s = s + \overline{PQ} \sin \phi, \qquad s' + \delta s' = s' - \overline{PQ} \sin \phi',$$

so that Fermat's principle reduces to

$$\mu \sin \phi = \mu' \sin \phi',$$

or Snell's law of refraction.

In principle we could continue to follow the progress of a ray down the z-axis, as it encounters one refracting surface after another, and eventually determine its height and direction when it emerges from the last surface. But let us stop and examine what happens to such a ray between the time it strikes the first surface until it emerges from the last. It is first bent, then translated, then bent, translated, and so on.

Given the height and direction cosine of the incoming ray, it would be most convenient to replace the sometimes very complicated optical instrument by an operator which would yield the height and direction cosine of the emergent ray. If this were possible, it would be a simple matter to proceed one step backward from the first surface to the object plane and one step forward from the last surface to the image plane. We would then have an operator which describes the transformation from the position and direction of the ray leaving the object plane to the position and direction of the ray entering the image plane. It is then natural to ask what properties the operator must have so that all rays (independent of direction) leaving the object plane at a height x, image at x', except possibly for a change of scale (magnification β'). The answer to this question defines the *image plane*. Further, we may ask under what conditions can a plane be imaged at unit magnification ($\beta' = 1$). The answer will determine the *unit planes* or *principal planes*. Finally, we can determine the properties of the operator, such that a ray leaving the object axial point at an angle α impinge on the image axial point at the same angle $\alpha' = \alpha$. This will locate the *nodal planes*. Thus the operator would contain all information concerning the location of the *cardinal planes* and *cardinal points* (intersection of the cardinal planes with the optical axis).

3–2 Sign convention

We do not have to look far for operators to perform these transformations. Matrix algebra is ideally suited to handle problems such as these. Clearly there are two basic operations involved; refraction* and translation. We now proceed to derive the refraction and translation matrices **R** and **T**, respectively. Before doing so, we state the following sign convention:

   1. Unless otherwise stated, the light always proceeds from left to right.

   2. A distance is positive if measured from left to right.

   3. A distance is always measured from a refracting surface.

   4. The vertex of a refracting surface is its intersection point with the axis of symmetry of the system.

   5. A radius of curvature is positive if the direction from the vertex to the center of curvature is from left to right.

   6. A ray coordinate before and after refraction will be denoted by the same letter; the one after refraction will be primed.

   7. Indices will be used to indicate at what surface the refraction is taking place. The numbering of the surfaces will be in the order in which the light is passing through them.

3–3 Refraction matrix

Consider the incident and refracted ray in Fig. 3–2. For simplicity we consider rays only in the xz-plane ($y = 0$). The method can be applied directly to rays out of that plane; we shall list the results, at the end of this section, for a ray striking the surface at a point (x, y, z), with direction cosines l, m, n. We designate the radius of curvature of the spherical refracting surface by $r = PC$, and we define $R = 1/r$ as the curvature.

---

* Henceforth we will treat reflection as a special case of refraction by inserting a negative index in Snell's law.

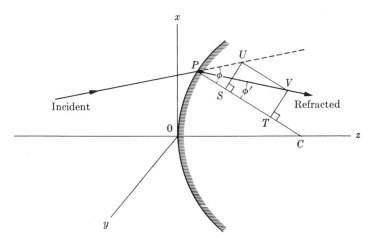

<figure>FIGURE 3–2</figure>

We now construct*

$$PU = \mu, \qquad PV = \mu',$$

then

$$US = \mu \sin \phi, \qquad VT = \mu' \sin \phi',$$

and

$$US = VT$$

by Snell's law. Thus UV and PC are parallel and have in common the direction cosine

$$\cos \alpha = \frac{0 - x}{r} = -xR.$$

Next we consider the projection of the PVU triangle on the x-axis (Fig. 3–3),

$$\mu l = \mu' l' + UV \cos (\pi - \alpha),$$

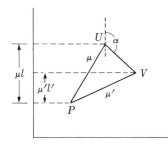

<figure>FIGURE 3–3</figure>

* That is, using arbitrary units, we mark off a length PU equal to the index.

or by rearranging, we have

$$\mu'l' = \mu l + UV \cos \alpha = \mu l - UV \frac{x}{r}.$$

However, since

$$UV = PT - PS = \mu' \cos \phi' - \mu \cos \phi,$$

we have

$$\mu'l' = \mu l - Ax,$$

where

$$A = \frac{\mu' \cos \phi' - \mu \cos \phi}{r}$$

is called the *power* of the surface. It is convenient now to define "optical direction cosines" by the relations

$$L = \mu l, \qquad L' = \mu'l';$$

and since $x' = x$ before and after refraction, the transformation equation for refraction is given by

$$\begin{pmatrix} L' \\ x' \end{pmatrix} = \begin{pmatrix} 1 & -A \\ 0 & 1 \end{pmatrix} \begin{pmatrix} L \\ x \end{pmatrix},$$

where the refraction matrix **R** is given by

$$\mathbf{R} = \begin{pmatrix} 1 & -A \\ 0 & 1 \end{pmatrix}.$$

3–4 Translation matrix

Let us now describe the translation of a ray from one surface to the next after bending. It turns out to be convenient to define* a "reduced distance" $\boldsymbol{T}_i' = T_i'/\mu'$, where T_i' is the geometrical length of the ray, and the prime indicates that refraction has taken place; the subscript refers to the ith surface. From Fig. 3–4, we see that

$$x_{i+1} = x_i + ps \cos \alpha = x_i + T_i'l_i', \qquad \text{or} \qquad x_{i+1} = x_i + \boldsymbol{T}_i'L_i';$$

but we note that since

$$l_i' = l_{i+1}, \qquad \mu_i' = \mu_{i+1}, \qquad \text{then} \qquad L_i' = L_{i+1},$$

so that from one surface to the next

$$L_{i+1} = L_i', \qquad x_{i+1} = \boldsymbol{T}_i'L_i' + x_i,$$

---

* The reader should note that the boldface $\boldsymbol{T}$, $\boldsymbol{t}$, $\boldsymbol{\alpha}$, $\boldsymbol{l}$, and $\boldsymbol{s}$ incorporate the index of refraction of the medium.

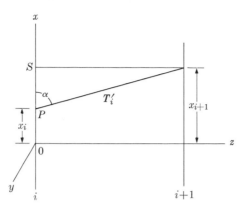

FIGURE 3–4

yielding a translation matrix

$$\mathbf{T} = \begin{pmatrix} 1 & 0 \\ T'_i & 1 \end{pmatrix}.$$

Consider now a complete system of refracting surfaces centered on the optical axis. The matrix describing the transformation of the height and direction of a ray from the first vertex V to the last vertex V' is given by

$$\mathbf{S}_{V'V} = \begin{pmatrix} 1 & -A_n \\ 0 & 1 \end{pmatrix} \begin{pmatrix} 1 & 0 \\ T'_{n-1} & 1 \end{pmatrix} \cdots \begin{pmatrix} 1 & 0 \\ T'_1 & 1 \end{pmatrix} \begin{pmatrix} 1 & -A_1 \\ 0 & 1 \end{pmatrix}$$

$$= \;_{V'}\!\begin{pmatrix} B & -A \\ -D & C \end{pmatrix}_V, \tag{3–2}$$

so that

$$\begin{pmatrix} L' \\ x' \end{pmatrix} = \;_{V'}\!\begin{pmatrix} B & -A \\ -D & C \end{pmatrix}_V \begin{pmatrix} L \\ x \end{pmatrix}. \tag{3–3}$$

Had we included rays out of the plane of the paper, we would proceed in the same fashion and at this point have in addition to Eq. (3–5), an equation of the form

$$\begin{pmatrix} M' \\ y' \end{pmatrix} = \begin{pmatrix} B & -A \\ -D & C \end{pmatrix} \begin{pmatrix} M \\ y \end{pmatrix},$$

where M is the optical direction cosine with respect to the y-axis. Since these results for y can be determined directly from those for x, we continue to confine our attention to rays in the xz-plane.

3-5 Paraxial approximation

There is a simple check on the matrix multiplication described in Eq. (3-2). Since the determinant of each translation and refraction matrix is unity, the determinant of the final **S** matrix is unity ($BC - AD = 1$). Furthermore, this is true at each step of the reduction process and offers a quick check on the calculations.

Unfortunately, nonlinear relations cause the basic elements, A and T', of these matrices to be different for each ray entering the system. For example, even in the usual sagitta approximation, the optical thickness is quadratic in the coordinates of the second-order refracting surfaces. Furthermore, Snell's law describes a linear relation in the sine of the incident and refracted angles while A, the power, contains the cosine of these angles. As a result, each A and T' are different for different rays.

To derive some general properties of lens systems, we must strike a compromise, which involves the consideration of only bundles of rays which lie along (paraxial) the axis of the system. What we gain in simplicity is offset by our inability to describe precisely what happens to rays away from the axis. In short, we are including in this first approximation, only the first term in the series expansions of A and T'.

In this "paraxial approximation" we now set

$$\cos \phi' \cong \cos \phi \cong 1, \qquad A \cong \frac{\mu' - \mu}{r} = a,$$

$$T' = t',$$

measured along the axis; and to remind us of this approximation, we replace the capital letters A, B, C, D with

$$\mathbf{S} = \begin{pmatrix} b & -a \\ -d & c \end{pmatrix}.$$

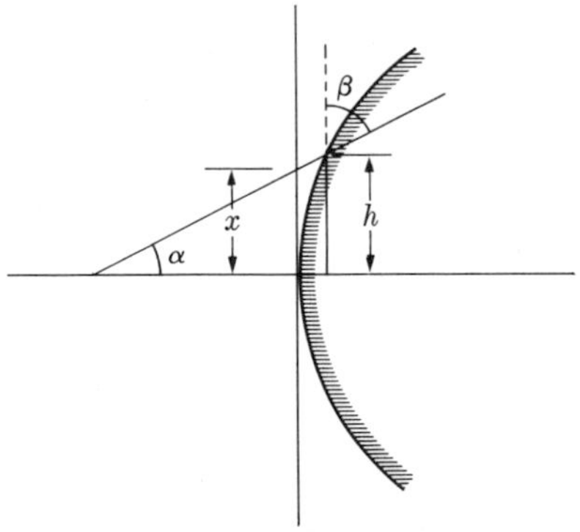

FIGURE 3-5

Furthermore, from Fig. 3–5 we introduce additional approximations,

$$l = \cos \beta = \sin \alpha \cong \alpha,$$
$$L = \mu l \cong \mu \alpha \equiv \alpha,$$
$$L' = \mu' l' \cong \alpha',$$
$$x \cong h = h'.$$

Our basic matrix transformations now become

$$\begin{pmatrix} \alpha'_i \\ h'_i \end{pmatrix} = \begin{pmatrix} 1 & -a \\ 0 & 1 \end{pmatrix} \begin{pmatrix} \alpha_i \\ h_i \end{pmatrix}, \qquad \begin{pmatrix} \alpha_{i+1} \\ h_{i+1} \end{pmatrix} = \begin{pmatrix} 1 & 0 \\ t'_i & 1 \end{pmatrix} \begin{pmatrix} \alpha'_i \\ h'_i \end{pmatrix}.$$

3–6 Image formation

It is now a simple matter to include the notion of image formation. Suppose we introduce two plane surfaces (Fig. 3–6), one to the left of the front vertex V and the other to the right of the rear vertex V'. Clearly the transformation of a ray between these planes can be described by two translation matrices in the form

$$\mathbf{S}_{P'P} = \begin{pmatrix} 1 & 0 \\ t'_n & 1 \end{pmatrix}_{V'} \begin{pmatrix} b & -a \\ -d & c \end{pmatrix}_V \begin{pmatrix} 1 & 0 \\ t'_0 & 1 \end{pmatrix},$$

where, in the light of the sign convention being used,

$$t'_0 = -l, \qquad t'_n = l';$$

l and l' are referred to the front and rear vertices, respectively. Now carrying out the matrix multiplication, we have

$$\begin{pmatrix} \alpha' \\ x' \end{pmatrix} = \begin{pmatrix} b + la & -a \\ bl' + all' - d - lc & c - l'a \end{pmatrix}_P \begin{pmatrix} \alpha \\ x \end{pmatrix}.$$

We now define the *image* of P by $x' = \beta' x$ for any angle α, where β' is a constant scale factor called the magnification. This implies that we set

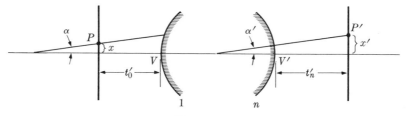

FIGURE 3–6

the lower left-hand element equal to zero and solve for

$$l' = \frac{lc + d}{la + b}.$$

Further,

$$\beta' = c - l'a = \frac{1}{b + la}, \tag{3-4}$$

which is due to the fact that the determinant value of the matrix must be unity. A negative β' merely refers to an inverted image.

We have then for the transformation of a ray between conjugate* planes

$$\begin{pmatrix} \alpha' \\ x' \end{pmatrix} = \begin{pmatrix} 1/\beta' & -a \\ 0 & \beta' \end{pmatrix} \begin{pmatrix} \alpha \\ x \end{pmatrix}, \tag{3-5}$$

where clearly

$$\beta' = \frac{x'}{x};$$

and for the axial ($x = 0$) conjugate points

$$\alpha' = \frac{\alpha}{\beta'}.$$

3–7 The cardinal points

Next we define the *unit* or *principal* planes (l_H, l'_H) as conjugate planes with a magnification of $\beta' = 1$. From Eq. (3–4), we have

$$c - l'_H a = 1 = b + l_H a,$$

or

$$l_H = \frac{1 - b}{a}, \qquad l'_H = \frac{c - 1}{a}.$$

These equations locate the unit planes in terms of the elements (a, b, c) of the system matrix $\mathbf{S}_{V'V}$. The *unit points* are the axial points of the unit planes, and since $\beta' = +1$, we see that for these points the reduced angles are the same ($\alpha' = \alpha$).

Suppose that we measure the object and image planes from the unit points instead of from the front and last surface. Then from Fig. 3–7 we see that†

$$l = s + l_H, \qquad l' = s' + l'_H,$$

---

* Those planes satisfying an object-image relation.

† It is important to remember that the numbers corresponding to these symbols will be negative when referred to the front vertex V.

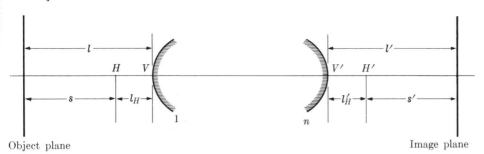

Object plane   Image plane

FIGURE 3–7

so that

$$\beta' = c - l'a = c - s'a - l'_H a = 1 - s'a,$$

and

$$\frac{1}{\beta'} = b + la = b + sa + l_H a = 1 + sa.$$

Hence in terms of distances measured from the unit points, the system matrix becomes

$$\mathbf{S} = \begin{pmatrix} 1 + sa & -a \\ 0 & 1 - s'a \end{pmatrix},$$

and, since the determinant is still unity,

$$(1 + sa)(1 - s'a) = 1$$

or, in a slightly more familiar form

$$\frac{1}{s'} = \frac{1}{s} + a, \tag{3–6}$$

which is the simple lens formula. Further, solving the equations $\beta' = 1 - s'a$ and $1/\beta' = 1 + sa$ for s and s', we find

$$\beta' = \frac{s'}{s}. \tag{3–7}$$

Let us now turn to an interpretation of the elements (a, b, c, d) of the system matrix. These quantities are known as the Gaussian constants of the system. From the fact that the determinant value must be unity, we need only investigate three of these quantities.

First, by letting the object and image distances (s, s') approach infinity in Eq. (3–6), we determine a in terms of the back and front focal distances f', f, respectively:

$$a = \frac{1}{f'} = -\frac{1}{f},$$

or eliminating a,

$$f' = -\frac{\mu'}{\mu} f.$$

By letting $s \to \infty$ in Eq. (3–7), we see that $\beta' \to 0$ and the back focal length l'_F, measured from the rear vertex from Eq. (3–4), is

$$l'_F = \frac{c}{a} = cf'.$$

Similarly, $1/\beta' \to 0$ as $s' \to \infty$, yielding from Eq. (3–4) again the expression for the front focal length l_F measured from the front vertex

$$l_F = -\frac{b}{a} = bf.$$

Thus b and c describe what fraction of the focal lengths lie outside the lens, and, indirectly, where the unit points are located.

The *nodal points* l_N, l'_N of an optical system are defined as conjugate points along the axis for which rays passing through these points make the same angle $\alpha' = \alpha$ with the axis of symmetry. Letting $x = 0$ in Eq. (3–5), we find that by setting

$$\frac{\alpha'}{\alpha} = \frac{\mu}{\beta'\mu'} = 1 \qquad \text{or} \qquad \beta' = \frac{\mu}{\mu'} = c - l'_N a = \frac{1}{b + l_N a},$$

we can solve for l_N and l'_N in the form

$$l_N = \frac{(\mu/\mu') - b}{a}, \qquad l'_N = \frac{c - (\mu/\mu')}{a},$$

so that in air, the nodal and unit points coincide. The unit, or principal, and nodal points as a group are often referred to as the *cardinal* points of the system.

3–8 Illustrations*

We shall now attempt to illustrate the use of the matrices in several representative cases. It is important to bear in mind that when tracing a bundle of paraxial rays through the systems graphically, parallel rays in one space pass through the conjugate focal point, that a ray striking the front unit plane l_H will emerge at the back unit plane l'_H at the same height (since these planes are imaged at $+1$ magnification), and finally that a ray making an angle α with the front nodal point will emerge from the back nodal point making the same angle with the optic axis.

---

*All dimensions in these figures are in centimeters, and we remind the reader that the boldface T, t, α, l, and s here incorporate the index of refraction of the medium.

TABLE 3–1

r	μ	μ'	t'	$\bar{t}'$	$\mu' - \mu$	a
13.79	1.000	1.6203	0.290	0.1790	0.6203	0.04498
6.102	1.6203	1.5728	0.590	0.3751	−0.0475	−0.00778
125.5	1.5728	1.0000			−0.5728	−0.00456

EXAMPLE 1. *Telescope doublet.* Given the radii, indices of refraction, and separations in Table 3–1, one proceeds to calculate the system matrix as follows.

$$\mathbf{S} = \begin{pmatrix} b & -a \\ -d & c \end{pmatrix} = \begin{pmatrix} 1 & -a_3 \\ 0 & 1 \end{pmatrix} \begin{pmatrix} 1 & 0 \\ t'_2 & 1 \end{pmatrix} \begin{pmatrix} 1 & -a_2 \\ 0 & 1 \end{pmatrix} \begin{pmatrix} 1 & 0 \\ t'_1 & 1 \end{pmatrix} \begin{pmatrix} 1 & -a_1 \\ 0 & 1 \end{pmatrix};$$

$$\mathbf{S} = \begin{pmatrix} 1 & 0.00456 \\ 0 & 1 \end{pmatrix} \begin{pmatrix} 1 & 0 \\ 0.3751 & 1 \end{pmatrix} \begin{pmatrix} 1 & 0.00778 \\ 0 & 1 \end{pmatrix} \begin{pmatrix} 1 & 0 \\ 0.179 & 1 \end{pmatrix} \begin{pmatrix} 1 & -0.04498 \\ 0 & 1 \end{pmatrix};$$

$$\mathbf{S} = \begin{pmatrix} b & -a \\ -d & c \end{pmatrix} = \begin{pmatrix} 1.0039 & -0.0328 \\ 0.5546 & 0.9780 \end{pmatrix};$$

$$f = -\frac{1}{a} = -30.488, \qquad f' = \frac{1}{a} = 30.488,$$

$$l_H = \frac{1-b}{a} = -0.1189, \qquad l'_H = \frac{c-1}{a} = -0.6707,$$

$$l_F = -\frac{b}{a} = -30.607, \qquad l'_F = \frac{c}{a} = 29.817.$$

The diagram is shown in Fig. 3–8.

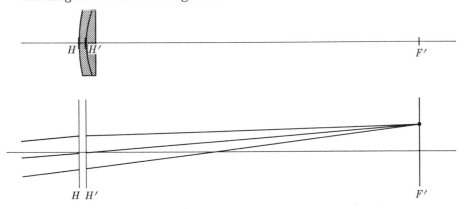

FIG. 3–8. Telescope doublet.

TABLE 3–2

r	μ	μ'	t'	t'	$\mu' - \mu$	a
∞	1.0000	1.5273	0.350	0.2292	0.5273	0.0
-1.890	1.5273	1.0000	2.230	2.230	-0.5273	0.27899
1.645	1.0000	1.5273	0.250	0.1637	0.5273	0.32055
∞	1.5273	1.0000			-0.5273	0.0

EXAMPLE 2. *Ramsden eyepiece.* Given the indices of refraction, separations, and radii in Table 3–2 we have for the system matrix

$$\mathbf{S} = \begin{pmatrix} b & -a \\ -d & c \end{pmatrix} = \begin{pmatrix} 1 & -a_4 \\ 0 & 1 \end{pmatrix}\begin{pmatrix} 1 & 0 \\ t'_3 & 1 \end{pmatrix}\begin{pmatrix} 1 & -a_3 \\ 0 & 1 \end{pmatrix}\begin{pmatrix} 1 & 0 \\ t'_2 & 1 \end{pmatrix}\begin{pmatrix} 1 & -a_2 \\ 0 & 1 \end{pmatrix}\begin{pmatrix} 1 & 0 \\ t'_1 & 1 \end{pmatrix}\begin{pmatrix} 1 & -a_1 \\ 0 & 1 \end{pmatrix};$$

$$\mathbf{S} = \begin{pmatrix} 1 & 0 \\ 0 & 1 \end{pmatrix}\begin{pmatrix} 1 & 0 \\ 0.1637 & 1 \end{pmatrix}\begin{pmatrix} 1 & -0.32055 \\ 0 & 1 \end{pmatrix}\begin{pmatrix} 1 & 0 \\ 2.230 & 1 \end{pmatrix}\begin{pmatrix} 1 & -0.27899 \\ 0 & 1 \end{pmatrix}\begin{pmatrix} 1 & 0 \\ 0.2292 & 1 \end{pmatrix}\begin{pmatrix} 1 & 0 \\ 0 & 1 \end{pmatrix};$$

$$\mathbf{S} = \begin{pmatrix} b & -a \\ -d & c \end{pmatrix} = \begin{pmatrix} 0.1935 & -0.4001 \\ 2.3482 & 0.3124 \end{pmatrix};$$

$$f = -\frac{1}{a} = -2.499, \qquad f' = \frac{1}{a} = 2.499,$$

$$l_H = \frac{1-b}{a} = 2.016, \qquad l'_H = -1.719,$$

$$l_F = -\frac{b}{a} = -0.483, \qquad l'_F = \frac{c}{a} = 0.780.$$

The corresponding ray diagram is shown in Fig. 3–9.

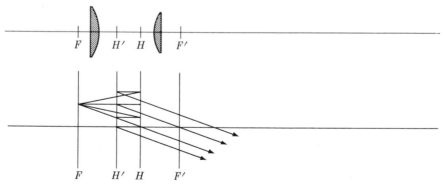

FIG. 3–9. Ramsden eyepiece.

TABLE 3–3

r	μ	μ'	t'
1.628	1.0000	1.6116	0.357
−27.57	1.6116	1.0000	0.189
−3.457	1.0000	1.6053	0.081
1.582	1.6053	1.0000	0.325
∞	1.0000	1.5123	0.217
1.920	1.5123	1.6116	0.396
−2.400	1.6116	1.0000	

EXAMPLE 3. *Tessar lens.* Given the indices of refraction, separations, and radii in Table 3–3, we calculate

$$a = 0.1968, \qquad c = 0.8675,$$
$$b = 0.8489, \qquad d = -1.3387,$$

then we proceed to calculate unit and focal planes.

Unit planes:
$$l_H = 0.7678,$$
$$l'_H = -0.6733.$$

Focal planes:
$$f = -5.082,$$
$$f' = 5.082.$$

Figure 3–10 shows the lens diagram for this case.

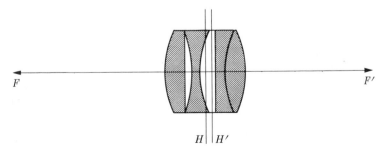

F F'

H H'

FIG. 3–10. Tessar lens.

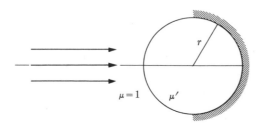

FIGURE 3–11

EXAMPLE 4.

This is an enlightening example for the reader interested in testing his knowledge of the sign convention. The optical system shown in Fig. 3–11 consists of a solid glass sphere of index μ' silvered on the back side to render that surface reflecting. One must invoke here that among other rules explicitly stated earlier, distance measured along the direction with which the light leaves the object plane is positive. Carefully noting the sign of each term, we proceed with the calculation of the system matrix as follows:

$$\mathbf{S} = \begin{pmatrix} 1 & -\left[\dfrac{-1-(-\mu')}{r}\right] \\ 0 & 1 \end{pmatrix} \begin{pmatrix} 1 & 0 \\ \dfrac{-2r}{-\mu'} & 1 \end{pmatrix} \begin{pmatrix} 1 & -\dfrac{-\mu'-\mu'}{-r} \\ 0 & 1 \end{pmatrix} \begin{pmatrix} 1 & 0 \\ \dfrac{2r}{\mu'} & 1 \end{pmatrix} \begin{pmatrix} 1 & -\left[\dfrac{\mu'-1}{r}\right] \\ 0 & 1 \end{pmatrix},$$

$$\mathbf{S} = \begin{pmatrix} b & -a \\ -d & c \end{pmatrix} = \begin{pmatrix} \dfrac{\mu'-4}{\mu'} & -\dfrac{2}{\mu'}\left(\dfrac{2-\mu'}{r}\right) \\ \dfrac{-4r}{\mu'} & \dfrac{\mu'-4}{\mu'} \end{pmatrix}.$$

Interesting special cases can now be worked out by assigning various values to μ'.

Before closing this discussion of paraxial optics, there is one further topic that deserves some attention. That has to do with the theory of pupils. Of the complete bundle of rays that emanate from an object point only a certain fraction enter the first refracting surface, make their way through the system, emerge at the last surface and converge on an image point. From the axial point of the object plane there is one aperture which most limits the bundle that passes through the system. To determine this limiting aperture, one images, in turn, each diaphragm to the right of the first surface in the system (including the edge of the lens) back into object space starting with the first surface. That limiting aperture whose conjugate in object space subtends the smallest angle as viewed from the axial object point is called the *entrance pupil E*. Its image in image space is called the *exit pupil E'*. The location of the entrance and exit pupils then is obviously a function of the location of the object plane. Even for a fixed object plane, as one moves away from the axis, the bundle of rays from off-axis points will be limited by different and sometimes more than one aperture. As one continues to move away from the axis, one will reach a stage when no rays will pass through the system. The ray from an off-axis point passing through the axial point of the entrance pupil is called the *principal ray* for this object point. Since, in general, one or more apertures within the system may obstruct the passage of this ray, only a fraction of the original bundle from that object point will partially fill the exit pupil. This effect is called *vignetting*. That region of the field for which the illumination at the edge is roughly one half that at the center defines the *field of view* of the instrument. The aperture which blocks the principal ray from an object point just beyond this is called the *object field stop*. Its conjugate in image space is the *image field stop*. Often it is possible to insert a lens that does not alter the object image relation but does improve the field of view. Such a lens is called a *field lens*.

REFERENCES

1. W. BROUWER, *Matrix Methods in Optical Instrument Design*. Benjamin (1963), in press.
2. G. C. STEWARD, *The Symmetrical Optical System*. Cambridge Tract (1928).

4

The Geometrical Theory of Aberrations

4-1 Wave aberration function

The question now arises as to how to handle the problem of image formation when higher-order terms are taken into account in the series expansion of A and T' in the basic $\mathbf{R}$ and $\mathbf{T}$ matrices. The succeeding corrections to paraxial optics lead in turn to third-, fifth-, seventh-, and higher-order aberration theory. The way in which these corrections combine when added from one surface to another is the basic problem of lens design. Fascinating as that subject may be, it would take us too far afield to enter into the details here. Suffice it to say that the advent of high speed computing machines, in principle, permits the designer to attempt more radical and sophisticated designs and has reduced to a minimum the tedious misuse of his own time in hand calculations. In practice, the machine can only obey orders, so it is the experience and ingenuity of the designer that determines the degree of precision which is attainable and consistent with the physical and economic constraints that are always present.

However, to give some attention to the geometrical theory of aberrations, we now adopt a phenomonological approach. With reference to Fig. 4-1, we now symbolically replace the actual optical system with the four planes representing the object, image, entrance, and exit pupil planes. Next we construct a sphere centered at P', which is the Gaussian image of P, of radius R passing through the center of the exit pupil and hence along the principal ray. Now if the optical path were the same for every ray leaving P, passing through the instrument, and emerging from the exit pupil, then the reference sphere would represent a surface of constant optical path, and all rays would converge on P'. In practice, the surface of constant optical path is not a sphere, and the amount by which it deviates from a sphere we shall call the aberration function $\Delta(u, v, h)$. Several representations of $\Delta(u, v, h)$ are possible, but here we will consider only a power series expansion and defer, until a later discussion, the possibility of employing an expansion in a complete set of functions orthogonal to a unit circle. Further, it is possible to show from symmetry arguments for the symmetrical optical system under discussion that in

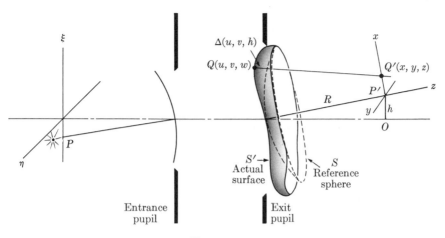

FIGURE 4–1

terms of the polar coordinates ρ and ϕ in the exit pupil, Δ can depend only upon the three rotational invariants h^2, ρ^2, $h\rho \cos \phi$. We then have for the general case

$$\Delta(\rho, \phi, h) = a_0 + b_0 h^2 + b_1 \rho^2 + b_2 h\rho \cos \phi + c_0 h^4 + c_1 \rho^4$$
$$|\; c_2 h^2 \rho^2 \cos^2 \phi + c_3 h^2 \rho^2 + c_4 h^3 \rho \cos \phi$$
$$+ c_5 h \rho^3 \cos \phi + d_0 h^6 + d_1 \rho^6 + \cdots, \qquad (4\text{–}1)$$

where

$$u = a\rho \cos \phi, \qquad \rho = \sqrt{(u^2 + v^2)/a^2}, \qquad 0 \leq \rho \leq 1,$$
$$v = a\rho \sin \phi, \qquad \phi = \tan^{-1} v/u, \qquad a = \text{radius of the}$$
$$\text{exit pupil.}$$

We merely point out here that the terms in b_1 and b_2 represent focusing adjustments, and those in c_1, c_2, c_3, c_4, c_5 represent, respectively, the classical aberrations of Seidel (spherical, astigmatism, field curvature, distortion, and coma). We will return to these points later and examine them in detail, but first we would like to know how the shape of this deformed surface causes the rays to deviate from the Gaussian image P'. To find the answer to this question, we shall digress a bit and examine the way in which one makes the passage from physical to geometrical optics.

4–2 Geometrical versus physical optics

The method is completely analogous to the WKB method of quantum mechanics. There one starts with a wave equation (the Schrödinger equation) and expands the phase of the ψ-function into a power series in Planck's constant h. In the zeroth-order approximation, one is left with the coefficient of h^0 for which the solution is the familiar Hamilton-Jacobi equation of classical mechanics

$$(\mathbf{grad}\ W)^2 = 2m(E - V),$$

where $\mathbf{grad}\ W$ is the linear momentum $\mathbf{p}$. One then examines in turn the first-, second-, and higher-order approximations.

In optics, we start with the wave equation,

$$\nabla^2 \phi(x, y, z, t) = \frac{\mu^2}{c^2} \frac{\partial^2 \phi}{\partial t^2}, \qquad \mu = \text{index of refraction}$$

whose solution can be expressed in the form

$$\phi(\mathbf{r}, t) = A(\mathbf{r}) \exp \{ik[L(\mathbf{r}) - ct]\}; \qquad A(\mathbf{r}) \text{ and } L(\mathbf{r}) \text{ are real.}$$

Replacing $A(\mathbf{r})$ by $\exp a(\mathbf{r})$ for convenience and noting that we can substitute into the wave equation the expressions

$$\nabla^2 \phi = \text{div } \mathbf{grad}\ \phi = [\nabla^2(a + ikL) + \{\mathbf{grad}\ (a + ikL)\}^2]\phi$$

and

$$-\frac{\mu^2}{c^2} \frac{\partial^2 \phi}{\partial t^2} = \mu^2 k^2 \phi,$$

we have

$$\{\nabla^2 a + (\mathbf{grad}\ a)^2 - k^2[(\mathbf{grad}\ L)^2 - \mu^2]\}$$
$$+ ik\{2\ (\mathbf{grad}\ a) \cdot (\mathbf{grad}\ L) + \nabla^2 L\} = 0.$$

Equating real and imaginary parts on both sides of the equation, we have

$$(\mathbf{grad}\ L)^2 - \mu^2 = \frac{\lambda^2}{4\pi^2} [\nabla^2 a + (\mathbf{grad}\ a)^2].$$

from the real part.* In the limit, as $\lambda \to 0$, we end up with the basic eikonal equation of geometrical optics,

$$(\mathbf{grad}\ L)^2 = \mu^2. \tag{4-2}$$

Hence surfaces of constant L are surfaces of constant optical phase, and thus they define the wave front. Further, the ray trajectories are normal

---

* Equating the imaginary parts yields a relation associated with an energy conservation principle.

to the wave surface. Since Eq. (4–2) is the result of an approximation, we cannot expect it to be rigorously true when the spatial changes in $a(\mathbf{r})$ are not negligible with respect to $1/\lambda$. Hence near a well-defined focus, where there exists a high concentration of light intensity, we must accept with serious reservations the predictions of geometrical optics.

4–3 Equations for the ray intercepts

Returning now to the exit pupil and bearing in mind the basic assumption of geometrical optics ($\lambda = 0$) so that we can invoke Eq. (4–2) there, we can now attempt to determine the equation of a straight line passing between $Q(u, v, w)$ and $Q'(x, y, z)$, with the additional constraint that it be normal to $\Delta(u, v, h)$ at Q. The equation of the actual wave surface S' is

$$u^2 + v^2 + w^2 = (R + \Delta)^2,$$

which reduces, of course, to the equation of the reference sphere for $\Delta = 0$. Since we shall be concerned, for the most part, with wave deformations expressed in units of the wavelength of light, here we shall neglect the term in Δ^2 leaving

$$u^2 + v^2 + w^2 - 2R\Delta - R^2 = 0. \tag{4–3}$$

Now the direction cosines of the unit vector

$$\mathbf{n} = \mathbf{i} \cos \alpha + \mathbf{j} \cos \beta + \mathbf{k} \cos \gamma$$

normal to this surface S' and the common unit vector of the line passing between Q and Q' are given by

$$\cos \alpha = \frac{u - R\,(\partial \Delta/\partial u)}{\frac{1}{2}|\mathbf{grad}\ S'|} = \frac{x - u}{\overline{QQ'}},$$

$$\cos \beta = \frac{v - R\,(\partial \Delta/\partial v)}{\frac{1}{2}|\mathbf{grad}\ S'|} = \frac{y - v}{\overline{QQ'}},$$

$$\cos \gamma = \frac{w}{\frac{1}{2}|\mathbf{grad}\ S'|} = \frac{z - w}{\overline{QQ'}}.$$

The equation of a ray leaving the exit pupil at Q, normal to the wave front and intersecting the receiving plane at Q', is given by

$$\frac{x - u}{u - R\,(\partial \Delta/\partial u)} = \frac{y - v}{v - R\,(\partial \Delta/\partial v)} = \frac{z - w}{w}$$

or, since in most applications,

$$w \cong -R \quad \text{and} \quad \frac{z}{|w|} \cong \frac{z}{R} \ll 1,$$

we have

$$x \cong -\frac{uz}{R} + R\frac{\partial \Delta}{\partial u}, \qquad y \cong -\frac{vz}{R} + R\frac{\partial \Delta}{\partial v}. \qquad (4\text{--}4)$$

In the Gaussian image plane ($z = 0$), Eqs. (4–4) reduce to the important equations

$$x_0 \cong R\frac{\partial \Delta}{\partial u}, \qquad y_0 \cong R\frac{\partial \Delta}{\partial v}. \qquad (4\text{--}5)$$

It is equally important to point out that, for the purposes of this section, here x and y refer to *deviations from* the Gaussian image point P'. The point ($x = 0 = y = z$) refers in general to an off-axis image P' not to the axial image point O. Finally, in polar coordinates ρ, ϕ, Eqs. (4–5) become

$$x_0 \cong \frac{R}{a}\left(\cos \phi \frac{\partial \Delta}{\partial \rho} - \frac{\sin \phi}{\rho} \frac{\partial \Delta}{\partial \phi}\right),$$

$$y_0 \cong \frac{R}{a}\left(\sin \phi \frac{\partial \Delta}{\partial \rho} + \frac{\cos \phi}{\rho} \frac{\partial \Delta}{\partial \phi}\right), \qquad (4\text{--}6)$$

so that, if in certain cases $\Delta \neq \Delta(\phi)$, a ring of rays $\rho = \text{const} = \rho_1$ will intersect the Gaussian receiving plane in a ring r_0 given by

$$r_0 = \sqrt{x_0^2 + y_0^2} = \frac{R}{a} \frac{\partial \Delta}{\partial \rho}\bigg|_{\rho=\rho_1} \qquad (4\text{--}7)$$

which is called the *transverse aberration*. The longitudinal spread along the axis, for this special case, can be determined in polar coordinates from Eq. (4–4) by setting $x = y = 0$. For a given ring in the exit pupil $\rho = \rho_1$, the longitudinal spread becomes

$$z = \frac{R^2}{a^2\rho} \frac{d\Delta}{d\rho}\bigg|_{\rho=\rho_1}, \qquad (4\text{--}8)$$

and the total effect can be determined by adding contributions from each annular ring $0 \leq \rho_1 \leq 1$.

Let us now proceed to examine in detail each term in the series expansion of Eq. (4–1).

1. *Constant terms.* Although such terms can certainly enter into the general expansion for Δ, we see, from Eqs. (4–5) and (4–6), that since they do not contain u and v and hence ρ and ϕ, these are not aberrations, since all the rays converge on $P'(x = 0 = y = z)$. In general, as we will see, the addition of a constant will not affect either the geometrical or physical optics predictions. The addition of a constant merely indicates that a reference sphere with a different radius, but with the same center has been chosen.

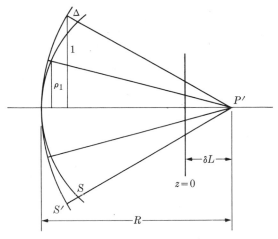

FIGURE 4–2

2. *Focusing errors.* (a) *Longitudinal:* $\Delta = b_1\rho^2$. Using Eqs. (4–7) and (4–8), we see that

$$r_0 = \frac{2b_1 R}{a}\rho_1, \qquad 0 \le \rho_1 \le 1,$$

$$z = \frac{2b_1 R^2}{a^2} = \delta L,$$

so that each ring in the exit pupil ρ_1 sweeps out a ring in the Gaussian image plane of radius $r_0 = (2b_1 R/a)\rho_1$ having a maximum dimension $(2b_1 R)/a$ for the edge rays (Fig. 4–2). However, all rays pass through the point $[0, 0, (2b_1 R^2)/a^2]$. Therefore, this is not an aberration but a longitudinal error in focusing. Conversely, had we started in focus at P' and moved out of focus by an amount δL, with respect to the new reference sphere drawn about the out-of-focus center, we would introduce a wave-front error of the form $b_1\rho^2$. The relation between b_1 and δL can be determined directly from a little geometry; from similar triangles

$$\frac{\delta L}{R} = \frac{2b_1 R}{a^2} = \frac{r_0}{a}.$$

This yields directly

$$b_1 = \frac{a^2\,\delta L}{2R^2}.$$

(b) *Transverse:*

$$\Delta = b_2 h\rho \cos\phi = \frac{b_2 h u}{a}.$$

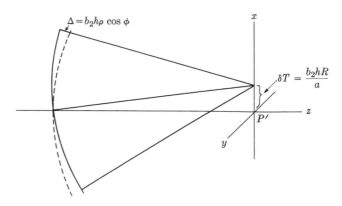

FIGURE 4–3

Using Eq. (4–5), we see that all rays converge on the point $[(b_2hR/a), 0, 0]$. Therefore, this is not an aberration either, and such a term merely describes a tipped wave front (Fig. 4–3). Conversely, had we moved from the Gaussian focus of a perfect system an amount δT transverse to the principal ray, then we would introduce a term of this form with $b_2h = (a\delta T)/R$.

3. *Seidel aberrations.* The next five terms in the power series expansion of Δ in Eq. (4–1) represent the classical third-order aberrations of Seidel; i.e., third order in the sense that differentiation reduces the combined exponent of h and ρ in this group from 4 to 3.

(a) *Spherical aberration:* This is the only third-order term existing on axis $h = 0$. Using Eqs. (4–7) and (4–8), we see that each annular ring ρ_1 produces its own ring in the Gaussian plane and crosses the axis at a point z, which is different for different zones. The maximum extent of these deviations for the marginal rays $\rho = 1$ is given by (Fig. 4–4)*

$$r_0 = \frac{4R}{a} c_1, \quad \text{and} \quad \delta L = \frac{4R^2}{a^2} c_1.$$

This effect can be offset somewhat by moving out of focus by an amount δf and viewing the wave-front deformation about the new reference sphere. Since, as we have seen,

$$c_1 = \frac{a^2}{4R^2} \delta L \quad \text{and} \quad b_1 = \frac{a^2}{2R^2} \delta f,$$

---

* It should be understood that, in this and in other examples, a negative sign in front of c_1 means that the actual wave front leads instead of lags the reference sphere, and hence the marginal rays would focus in front of the paraxial focus towards the exit pupil instead of away from the paraxial focus.

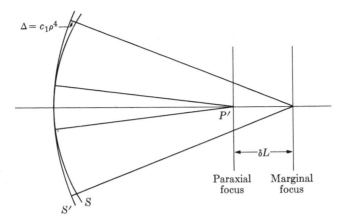

FIGURE 4–4

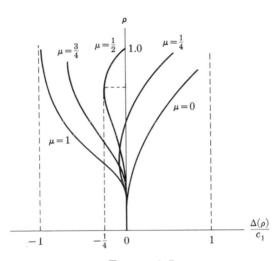

FIGURE 4–5

the wave deformation from the new receiving plane can be written as

$$\Delta(\rho) = c_1(\rho^4 - 2\mu\rho^2),$$

where

$$\mu = \frac{\delta f}{\delta L}$$

describes the position of the receiving plane: $\mu = 0$ corresponds to the paraxial focus; $\mu = 1$ corresponds to the marginal focus. The form of the wave deformation for various values of μ is shown in Fig. 4–5. Later, in our discussion of optical frequency response in the presence of aberrations, we shall attempt to find which of these focal positions is optimum. Suffice it to say here that elementary geometrical arguments lead to $\mu = \frac{1}{2}$; that is, the receiving plane should be midway between the marginal and paraxial focus.

(b) *Astigmatism and field curvature:*

$$\Delta = c_2 h^2 \rho^2 \cos^2 \phi + c_3 h^2 \rho^2.$$

These two are usually taken as a unit, and there is something to be gained by examining them in terms of cartesian coordinates u, v; that is,

$$\Delta = \frac{h^2}{a^2} [(c_2 + c_3) u^2 + c_3 v^2]$$

so that in the sagittal ($u = 0$) and tangential ($v = 0$) planes they appear as longitudinal focal errors; the wave front possesses a different curvature in these two planes. Using the general expression [Eq. (4-4)], we see in a plane removed a distance z from the Gaussian plane that

$$x = \left[-\frac{z}{R} + \frac{2Rh^2}{a^2} (c_2 + c_3) \right] u,$$

$$y = \left[-\frac{z}{R} + \frac{2Rh^2}{a^2} c_3 \right] v;$$

squaring and adding, we get

$$\frac{x^2}{[(z/R) - (2Rh^2/a^2)(c_2 + c_3)]^2} + \frac{y^2}{[(z/R) - (2Rh^2/a^2)c_3]^2} = a^2 \rho^2$$

so that each annular ring in the exit pupil produces, in general, an ellipse in the z- (receiving) plane.

The maximum dimensions of this ellipse occur for $\rho = 1$, and we have

$$\frac{x^2}{A^2} + \frac{y^2}{B^2} = 1,$$

where the semimajor and semiminor axes are given by

$$A = \left[z - \frac{2R^2h^2}{a^2} (c_2 + c_3) \right] \frac{a}{R},$$

$$B = \left[z - \frac{2R^2h^2}{a^2} c_3 \right] \frac{a}{R}.$$

Let us now determine the significance of c_2 and c_3. First, it is convenient to introduce a parameter σ defined by

$$\sigma = \frac{2R^2h^2}{a^2}.$$

Next we note that the pattern shrinks to a line ($A = 0$), where the rays in the tangential plane focus. The surface over which this occurs is given by

$$z_T = \sigma(c_2 + c_3).$$

Similarly, the rays in the sagittal plane ($u = 0$) come to a focus on a line over the surface described by

$$z_S = \sigma c_3;$$

the total spread between these focal lines is

$$z_T - z_S = \sigma c_2.$$

Thus we see the significance of c_2, which is the astigmatism coefficient. It describes the distance between the tangential and sagittal focal surfaces. Further, if $c_2 = 0$, then $A = B$, and $z_T = z_S$. The rays converge on a point, but that point deviates more and more from the Gaussian images as one moves away from the axis (h increasing). Hence we have the term "field curvature."

In the general case with c_2 and c_3 not zero, there is a surface z_c over which the pattern degenerates into a circle (the "circle of least confusion").* To determine this surface, we set $A^2 = B^2$ and solve for $z = z_c$. The result is

$$z_c = \frac{\sigma}{2}(2c_3 + c_2) \qquad \text{or} \qquad z_c = \frac{z_T + z_S}{2};$$

that is, the surface for the so-called "circle of least confusion" lies midway between the sagittal and tangential focal surfaces.

The whole situation is summarized in Fig. 4–6:

$$\frac{x^2}{(z - z_T)^2} + \frac{y^2}{(z - z_S)^2} = \frac{a^2}{R^2},$$

$$c_3 = \frac{z_S}{\sigma},$$

$$c_2 = \frac{z_T - z_S}{\sigma},$$

$$\sigma = \frac{2R^2 h^2}{a^2}.$$

(c) *Distortion:*

$$\Delta = c_4 h^3 \rho \cos \phi = \frac{c_4 h^3}{a} u.$$

---

* Later, the more precise physical optics description of the light distribution will cause us to abandon this quaint term. The actual light pattern, it turns out, will not be circular.

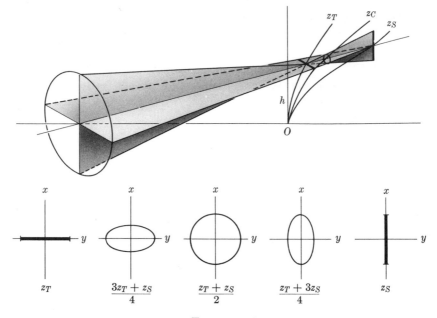

FIGURE 4–6

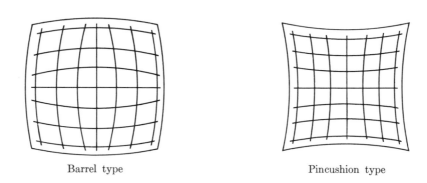

Barrel type   Pincushion type

FIGURE 4–7

Insofar as the dependence on the aperture coordinates is concerned, this term is the same as the transverse focal shift treated earlier, so that for a given field height h, all the rays focus on the point $[(R/a)c_4 h^3, 0, 0]$. However, this displacement varies as the cube of the field angle through h^3 and, depending upon the sign of c_4, leads to the familiar "barrel" or "pincushion" distortion of a grid object, as shown in Fig. 4–7.

(d) *Coma:*

$$\Delta = c_5 h \rho^3 \cos \phi.$$

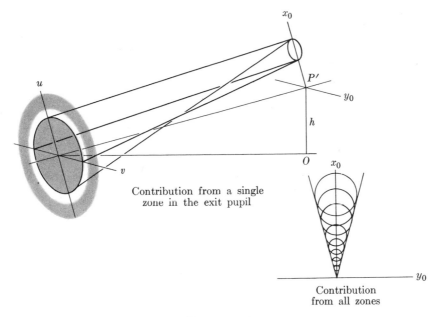

Contribution from a single
zone in the exit pupil

Contribution
from all zones

FIGURE 4–8

Substituting this expression into Eq. (4–6), we have

$$x_0 = \beta\rho^2(3\cos^2\phi + \sin^2\phi) = \beta\rho^2(2 + \cos 2\phi),$$
$$y_0 = \beta\rho^2(3\cos\phi\sin\phi - \cos\phi\sin\phi) = \beta\rho^2\sin 2\phi,$$

where

$$\beta = \frac{Rhc_5}{a}.$$

We can write these equations in a slightly different form:

$$(x_0 - 2\beta\rho^2) = \beta\rho^2\cos 2\phi, \qquad y_0 = \beta\rho^2\sin 2\phi.$$

Squaring and adding, we get

$$(x_0 - 2\beta\rho^2)^2 + y_0^2 = \beta^2\rho^4,$$

so that each annular ring in the exit pupil ($\rho = $ const) produces a circle in the Gaussian image plane whose center is along the x-axis and whose radius grows with increasing ρ and increasing field angle through β and h. Furthermore, because of the factor 2ϕ, a single traversal of an annular ring in the exit pupil corresponds to a double traversal of the circle in the image plane. The total contribution for all zones ($0 \leq \rho \leq 1$) results in the familiar coma flare, as shown in Fig. 4–8.

With this we end our introductory discussion of the geometrical properties of the Seidel aberrations. No attempt will be made to discuss the chromatic aberrations which introduce further interesting effects. Furthermore, we have purposely refrained from associating light intensity distributions with these geometrical patterns. The interested reader should consult the several excellent references [1, 2, 3] which graphically compare both these geometrical patterns, and the more accurate physical optics predictions with photographs of the point-image light distribution, in the presence of these aberrations taken singly.

4–4 Optimum balancing of third- and fifth-order spherical aberration

Insofar as the fifth-order terms are concerned, we confine our discussion to an interesting problem that often arises in practice. Suppose that we are on axis ($h = 0$), and the wave front, viewed slightly away from the Gaussian focal plane, is of the form

$$\Delta(\rho) = (b_1\rho^2 + c_1\rho^4 + d_1\rho^6). \tag{4–9}$$

From Eq. (4–8) the longitudinal aberration* δL, as seen from the paraxial focus ($b_1 = 0$), is

$$\delta L = \frac{1}{\sin^2 \alpha} \frac{1}{\rho} \frac{d\Delta}{d\rho}, \tag{4–10}$$

where $\sin \alpha \cong a/R$ is the sine of the semiaperture angle α. Using this same formula, we recall that if we move away from the paraxial focus an amount δf, then we must include the term $b_1\rho^2$ in Δ, where

$$b_1 = \frac{\delta f}{2} \sin^2 \alpha.$$

We now ask the following questions; what is the best balance to choose between the third- and fifth-order coefficients in the form c_1/d_1, say, and what is the optimum focal setting also in the form b_1/d_1? Clearly, the answer to these questions hinges critically on what criterion we use to describe such terms as "best" and "optimum." One criterion that is particularly useful and, as we will see later, has some foundation in physical optics also, is the minimum mean square [3] wave-front deformation.

Following Maréchal, we first calculate

$$\bar{\Delta} = \frac{1}{\pi(1)^2} \int_0^1 \int_0^{2\pi} \Delta(\rho)\rho \, d\rho \, d\phi. \tag{4–11}$$

---

*In the light of the assumption made in neglecting Δ^2 in Eq. (4–3), this formula is only approximately correct in fifth-order theory.

Next we form

$$E_0 = \overline{(\Delta - \bar{\Delta})^2} = \overline{\Delta^2} - (\bar{\Delta})^2, \tag{4-12}$$

where

$$\overline{\Delta^2} = \frac{1}{\pi} \int_0^1 \int_0^{2\pi} \Delta^2(\rho)\rho \, d\rho \, d\phi.$$

In general E_0 will be a function of b_1, c_1, and d_1. We next wish to determine the focal position ($\delta f \propto b_1$) that will minimize E_0. Thus setting

$$\frac{\partial E_0}{\partial b_1} = 0$$

and solving for $b_1 = b_1(c_1, d_1)$, we substitute this back into Eq. (4-12) which yields

$$(E_0)_{\text{min}} = E_0(c_1, d_1).$$

This expression can be further minimized to yield the optimum ratio c_1/d_1. For the problem under discussion, the application of Eqs. (4-11) and (4-12) to the wave-front error in Eq. (4-9) yields

$$E_0 = \frac{b_1^2}{12} + \frac{b_1 c_1}{6} + \frac{3 b_1 d_1}{20} + \frac{4 c_1^2}{45} + \frac{c_1 d_1}{6} + \frac{9 d_1^2}{112}. \tag{4-13}$$

Setting

$$\frac{\partial E_0}{\partial b_1} = 0,$$

we find

$$b_1 - -(c_1 + \tfrac{9}{10}d_1). \tag{4-14}$$

Now putting this back into Eq. (4-13), we get

$$(E_0)_{\text{min}} = \frac{c_1^2}{180} + \frac{c_1 d_1}{60} + \frac{9 d_1^2}{700}. \tag{4-15}$$

We can now introduce $\eta = c_1/d_1$ and minimize this expression with respect to η. The result is

$$\eta = \frac{c_1}{d_1} = -\frac{3}{2}, \tag{4-16}$$

and this, in turn, from Eq. (4-14), gives

$$\frac{b_1}{d_1} = \frac{3}{5}. \tag{4-17}$$

Equations (4-16) and (4-17) represent the answers to the original questions. Given the fifth-order coefficient d_1, the best balancing of the third-

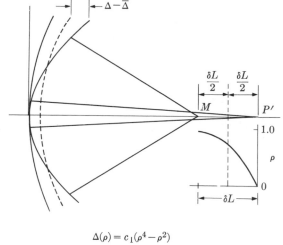

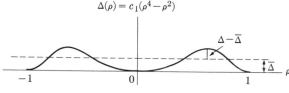

$$\Delta(\rho) = c_1(\rho^4 - \rho^2)$$

FIGURE 4-9

order coefficient and the focal setting, consistent with a minimum mean square wave-front deformation, should be chosen, such that

$$\Delta_{\text{opt}}(\rho) = d_1(\rho^6 - \tfrac{3}{2}\rho^4 + \tfrac{3}{5}\rho^2). \qquad (4\text{--}18)$$

To examine what this means near the image plane, we consider two special cases.

CASE 1. *Third-order spherical aberration only* $(d_1 = 0)$. Going back to Eqs. (4–13) through (4–15), setting $d_1 = 0$, and recalling the meaning of $\mu = \delta f/\delta L$ from our previous discussion concerning the Seidel aberrations, we have

$$\mu = \frac{\delta f}{\delta L} = -\frac{b_1}{2c_1} = \frac{1}{2}.$$

That is, from a position midway between the paraxial and marginal foci, the mean square wave-front deformation from the mean reference sphere is a minimum. (See Fig. 4–9.)

CASE 2. *Third- and fifth-order spherical aberration* $c_1, d_1 \neq 0$. From Eq. (4–10), we have

$$\delta L = \frac{2\rho^2}{\sin^2 \alpha} (2c_1 + 3d_1\rho^2), \qquad (4\text{--}19)$$

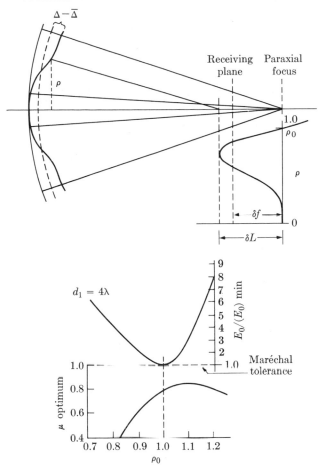

FIGURE 4–10

measured from the paraxial focus. There is a zone $\rho = \rho_0$ at which the wave front can be bent back to bring the rays back to the paraxial focus $[\delta L(\rho_0) = 0]$. From Eq. (4–19), this corresponds to

$$\frac{c_1}{d_1} = -\frac{3}{2}\rho_0^2.$$

The system is said to be under-, fully-, or over-corrected, depending on whether ρ_0 is greater than, equal to, or less than unity. (See Fig. 4–10.) For this ratio of c_1/d_1, Eq. (4–19) becomes

$$\delta L = \frac{6d_1\rho^2}{\sin^2\alpha}(\rho^2 - \rho_0^2),$$

which indicates that at $\rho = 0.707\rho_0$, we have

$$\delta L_{\max} = -\frac{3\rho_0^4}{2 \sin^2 \alpha} d_1$$

so that the third- and fifth-order wave-front coefficients are expressed in terms of the maximum longitudinal spherical aberration and state of correction.

Viewed from a plane slightly removed from the paraxial focus toward the lens by an amount $-\delta f$, the longitudinal aberration appears as

$$\delta L = \delta f - 4 \frac{\delta L_{\max}}{\rho_0^4} (\rho^4 - \rho_0^2\rho^2),$$

and the wave deformation as measured about the new reference sphere becomes

$$\Delta(\rho) = d_1(\rho^6 - \tfrac{3}{2}\rho_0^2\rho^4) + b_1\rho^2,$$

where, once again, we introduce the dimensionless parameter μ in the form

$$\mu = -\frac{\delta f}{\delta L_{\max}} = \frac{-2b_1/\sin^2 \alpha}{-(3\rho_0^4 d_1)/2 \sin^2 \alpha}$$

or

$$\frac{b_1}{d_1} = \frac{3}{4} \mu\rho_0^4$$

to indicate the position of the receiving plane. We now have

$$\Delta(\rho) = d_1(\rho^6 - \tfrac{3}{2}\rho_0^2\rho^4 + \tfrac{3}{4}\mu\rho_0^4\rho^2)$$

for the wave deformation as seen from $-\delta f$ in a state of correction ρ_0. Comparing this with the optimum expression in Eq. (4–18), we see that to achieve a minimum mean square wave-front deformation, we should first fully correct ($\rho_0 = 1$); that is, we should bring the marginal rays back to the paraxial focus and then focus ($\mu = \tfrac{4}{5}$) at 80% of the distance from the paraxial plane to the maximum zonal focus. The entire solution is summarized in Fig. 4–10.

4–5 The Maréchal method of aberration balancing

We now wish to generalize this procedure a bit. In doing so, we will include the nine fifth-order terms d_j, $j = 1, 2, \ldots 9$. However, since we are, in effect, standing at a fixed point in the field ($h = $ const), while averaging over the exit pupil, we will absorb all those terms which have similar dependence on the exit pupil coordinates into the third-order coefficients. This will have the effect of introducing only four new terms that are functionally different from the usual Seidel terms. Later, when passing to another field position, these coefficients can be unscrambled. Furthermore, to emphasize the notion of longitudinal and transverse focal shifts along and perpendicular to the principal ray, we make the following change in nomenclature:

$$L = b_1,$$
$$T = b_2 h.$$

We now proceed to outline the method. First, as seen from the Gaussian image point P', we start with $\Delta(\rho, \phi)$. By definition, the actual wave front matches the reference sphere at the center of the exit pupil $[\Delta(0, 0) = 0]$. Next, we move along and perpendicular to the principal ray an amount δz and δx, such that the wave deformation as seen from Q' (but still matching the wave front at the origin) is given by

$$\Delta'(\rho, \phi) = L\rho^2 + T\rho \cos \phi + \Delta(\rho, \phi),$$

where it is not difficult to show [4] that

$$L = - (1 - \cos \alpha) \, \delta z \cong - \frac{\alpha^2}{2} \, \delta z,$$
$$T = - \sin \alpha \, \delta x \cong -\alpha \, \delta x.$$

Now calculating

$$\overline{\Delta'} = \overline{\Delta'}(L, T, c_i, d_j, h), \qquad i = 1, \ldots, 5, \quad j = 1, \ldots, 9,$$

from

$$\overline{\Delta'} = \frac{1}{\pi} \int_0^1 \int_0^{2\pi} \Delta'(\rho, \phi)\rho \, d\rho \, d\phi,$$

we form

$$\Delta''(\rho, \phi) = \Delta' - \overline{\Delta'}$$

which represents the deformation of the wave front about the mean reference sphere $(\overline{\Delta''} = 0)$. Now, we define the mean square deformation

$$E_0 = \overline{(\Delta'')^2} = \overline{(\Delta')^2} - (\overline{\Delta'})^2 \qquad (4\text{–}20)$$

which, in general, is a function of L, T, h, c_i and d_j; we minimize it by setting

$$\frac{\partial E_0}{\partial L} = 0 = \frac{\partial E_0}{\partial T}.$$

The solutions to this pair of equations yield

$$\left. \begin{array}{l} L = L(c_i, d_j, h), \\ T = T(c_i, d_j, h), \end{array} \right| \quad \begin{array}{l} i = 1, 2, \ldots 5, \\ j = 1, 2, \ldots 9, \end{array} \qquad (4\text{–}21)$$

TABLE 4-1

L'	$L + c_3$
T'	$T + c_4$
C_1	$c_1 + d_2 h^2$
C_2	$c_2 h^2 + d_8 h^4$
C_3	$c_3 h^2 + d_3 h^4$
C_4	$c_4 h^3 + d_6 h^5$
C_5	$c_5 h + d_5 h^3$
D_1	d_1
D_4	$d_4 h$
D_7	$d_7 h^2$
D_9	$d_9 h^3$

or, since these equations are linearly related to δx and δz, they define a surface in image space over which the mean square wave-front deformation is a minimum. Substitution of L and T from Eq. (4–21) back into Eq. (4–20) results in

$$(E_0)_{\min} = E_0(c_i, d_j, h). \tag{4–22}$$

These results are by no means trivial. For small aberrations, Maréchal has shown that the Strehl definition of classical physical optics, and hence the total volume under the optical frequency response, is a direct function of E_0. Later we will investigate these points in detail. Here it is sufficient to say that it makes considerable sense to impose tolerances on the complete wave front taken as a whole, rather than on each aberration term separately.

It is also important to stress that the inaccuracies inherent in passing from the wave front in the exit pupil to the distribution of light intensity in the image plane, using geometrical optics, are not implied here. The term Δ, representing the optical path difference (opd) from a reference sphere, can be quite accurately determined. The fact that certain averages of Δ in E_0 are directly related to more precise physical optics estimates of the light distribution justifies the space devoted to it here.

To complete this section, we shall now apply these notions to a simple system; that of a single reflecting surface. In doing so, we shall maintain terms up to the fifth order. Consider then the expansion into the two focusing terms, the five third-order terms and the nine fifth-order terms. If we now collect like coefficients in $\rho^m \cos^n \phi$ then Δ' can be expressed as

$$
\begin{aligned}
\Delta'(\rho, \phi) = L'\rho^2 &+ T'\rho \cos \phi + C_1\rho^4 + C_2\rho^2 \cos^2 \phi \\
&+ C_5\rho^3 \cos \phi + D_1\rho^6 + D_4\rho^5 \cos \phi \qquad (4\text{--}23) \\
&+ D_7\rho^4 \cos^2 \phi + D_9\rho^3 \cos^3 \phi + \cdots,
\end{aligned}
$$

where the relation between the new and old coefficients are given in Table 4–1. In the following discussion, it is clear that by setting $d_j = 0$, $j = 1, 2, \ldots 9$, all formulas should reduce to the third-order case [1]. To avoid the rather lengthy mathematical details, we now assume that $\overline{(\Delta')^2}$ and $\overline{(\Delta')^2}$ have been calculated and substituted for E_0 in Eq. (4–20). Setting

$$
\frac{\partial E_0}{\partial L} = 0 = \frac{\partial E_0}{\partial T}
$$

we get

$$
L = -\left(C_1 + \frac{1}{2}C_2 + C_3 + 9\frac{D_1}{10} + \frac{D_7}{2} \right),
$$
$$
\qquad (4\text{--}24)
$$
$$
T = -\left(C_4 + \frac{2}{3}C_5 + \frac{D_4}{2} + \frac{D_9}{2} \right).
$$

By substituting these back into the expression for E_0, we have

$$
\begin{aligned}
(E_0)_{\min} = \frac{C_1^2}{180} &+ \frac{C_1D_1}{60} + \frac{C_1D_7}{180} + \frac{C_2^2}{24} + \frac{C_2D_7}{16} \\
&+ \frac{C_5^2}{72} + \frac{C_5D_4}{30} + \frac{C_5D_9}{48} + \frac{9D_1^2}{700} \qquad (4\text{--}25) \\
&+ \frac{D_1D_7}{120} + \frac{D_4^2}{48} + \frac{19D_7^2}{720} + \frac{D_9^2}{64} \\
&+ \frac{D_4D_9}{40}.
\end{aligned}
$$

We postpone the question of what tolerance to impose on $(E_0)_{\min}$ until later in our discussion of diffraction theory. We turn instead to the problem of evaluating these coefficients for a single spherical reflecting surface to illustrate the way in which the various terms enter into the expression for the optical path difference Δ. In more complicated systems, terms like these will enter at each surface, and it is the task of the lens designer to find convenient forms in which to add these contributions from surface to surface, in such a way that he can manipulate them later to achieve some compromise.

4–6 An illustration, a single reflecting surface

Consider then Fig. 4–11. Let $B(-h, 0, l)$ represent a self-luminous point of light and $B'(+h', 0, l')$ the receiving point. We shall see shortly the conditions under which we call B' the *image* of B. Since the entire medium to the right of the mirror is in air, the optical path difference is given by

$$\Delta = [BP + PB'] - [BO + OB']$$
$$= [BP - BO] + [PB' - OB']. \tag{4-26}$$

We now proceed to concentrate on the first bracketed term. Whatever we obtain for it will hold for the second term in the brackets by merely replacing l by l' and h by $-h'$. First

$$\overline{BO} = \sqrt{l^2 + h^2} = l\sqrt{1 + \tan^2 \theta}$$

and the expansion into a binomial series yields

$$\overline{BO} = l + \frac{l}{2}\tan^2 \theta - \frac{l}{8}\tan^4 \theta + \frac{l}{16}\tan^6 \theta + \cdots \tag{4-27}$$

As for $\overline{BP}$, we see that

$$(\overline{BP})^2 = (u + h)^2 + v^2 + (w - l)^2$$
$$= u^2 + v^2 + w^2 - 2lw + 2hu + h^2 + l^2,$$

but the equation of the sphere is

$$u^2 + v^2 + (w - R)^2 = R^2 \quad \text{or} \quad w = \frac{u^2 + v^2 + w^2}{2R} = \frac{s^2}{2R},$$

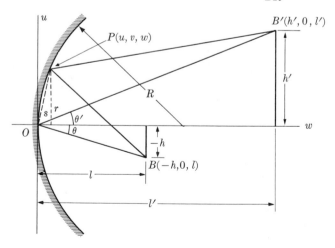

Figure 4–11

so that Eq. (4–28) can be written as

$$\overline{BP} = l\sqrt{1 + C} = l + \frac{l}{2}C - \frac{lC^2}{8} + \frac{lC^3}{16} + \cdots, \qquad (4\text{–}28)$$

where

$$C = \frac{Qs^2}{l} + \tan^2 \theta + \frac{2u \tan \theta}{l} \qquad \text{and} \qquad Q = \frac{1}{l} - \frac{1}{R}.$$

Now, maintaining terms in the combined power of u and h up to the sixth, we subtract Eq. (4–27) from Eq. (4–28) to get the first term in the brackets in Eq. (4–26). We now repeat the process for the second term and replace l by l', h by $-h'$, and, naturally, Q by $Q' = (1/l') - (1/R)$. Finally, adding the two bracketed terms and collecting coefficients in like powers of $u^m h^n$, we have

$$\Delta = \frac{s^2}{2}(Q + Q') + u(\tan \theta - \tan \theta') - \frac{s^4}{8}\left(\frac{Q^2}{l} - \frac{Q'^2}{l'}\right)$$

$$- \frac{u^2}{2}\left(\frac{\tan^2 \theta}{l} + \frac{\tan^2 \theta'}{l'}\right) - \frac{s^2}{4}(Q \tan^2 \theta + Q' \tan^2 \theta')$$

$$- \frac{s^2 u}{2}\left(\frac{Q}{l}\tan \theta - \frac{Q'}{l'}\tan \theta'\right) - \frac{u}{2}(\tan^3 \theta - \tan^3 \theta')$$

$$+ \frac{s^2}{16}\left(\frac{Q^3}{l^2} + \frac{Q'^3}{l'^2}\right) + \frac{u^3}{2}\left(\frac{\tan^3 \theta}{l^2} - \frac{\tan^3 \theta'}{l'^2}\right) + \frac{3u}{8}(\tan^5 \theta - \tan^5 \theta')$$

$$+ \frac{3u^2}{4}\left(\frac{\tan^4 \theta}{l} - \frac{\tan^4 \theta'}{l'}\right) + \frac{3s^2}{16}(Q \tan^4 \theta + Q' \tan^4 \theta')$$

$$+ \frac{3s^2 u}{4}\left(\frac{Q}{l}\tan^3 \theta - \frac{Q'}{l'}\tan^3 \theta'\right) + \frac{3s^4}{16}\left(\frac{Q^2}{l}\tan^2 \theta + \frac{Q'^2}{l'}\tan^2 \theta'\right)$$

$$+ \frac{3s^4 u}{8}\left(\frac{Q^2}{l^2}\tan \theta - \frac{Q'^2}{l'^2}\tan \theta'\right) + \frac{3s^2 u^2}{4}\left(\frac{Q}{l^2}\tan^2 \theta + \frac{Q'}{l'^2}\tan^2 \theta'\right)$$

$$+ \cdots.$$

At this time we impose the condition that B' be the image of B by setting the leading terms, in this series, equal to zero (the coefficients of the two focal error terms). That is, we demand that

$$Q + Q' = 0, \qquad \tan \theta = \tan \theta'.$$

These equations define the Gaussian image point in the form

$$\frac{1}{l'} + \frac{1}{l} = \frac{2}{R} \qquad \text{(the mirror formula)},$$
$$\theta' = \theta. \tag{4\text{–}29}$$

Substituting these values for θ', l' and hence $\tan \theta'$, Q' back into the series, we can determine the third- and fifth-order aberration coefficients for the mirror. Before proceeding, however, we introduce one more simplifying condition by letting the object point go to infinity so that $l' = R/2 = f'$. In addition, to cast the result into the form of Eq. (4–23), we introduce

$$\rho^2 = \frac{u^2 + v^2}{a^2} \simeq \frac{s^2}{a^2},$$

$$u = a\rho \cos \phi.$$

We then have

$$\Delta(\rho, \phi) = \frac{a^4}{4R^3} (\tfrac{3}{2} \tan^2 \theta - 1)\rho^4 + \frac{a^2 \tan^2 \theta}{R} (\tfrac{3}{2} \tan^2 \theta - 1)\rho^2 \cos^2 \phi$$

$$+ \frac{a^3 \tan \theta}{R^3} (1 - \tfrac{3}{2} \tan^2 \theta)\rho^3 \cos \phi + \frac{a^6}{4R^5} \rho^6$$

$$- \frac{3a^5 \tan \theta}{2R^4} \rho^5 \cos \phi + \frac{3a^4 \tan^2 \theta}{R^3} \rho^4 \cos^2 \phi$$

$$- \frac{2a^3 \tan^3 \theta}{R^2} \rho^3 \cos^3 \phi,$$

where we obtain the C and D coefficients by a direct comparison with Eq. (4–23). Once these coefficients are given, L and T and hence δx and δz, along with $(E_0)_{\min}$ can be determined from Eqs. (4–24) and (4–25), as a function of field angle and $F^\# = f'/2a$. Thus, once a meaningful tolerance has been established, it will be possible to determine the maximum allowable field angle for a given $F^\#$, together with the surface (δx, δz) over which the tolerance can be satisfied.

4–7 Zernike polynomials

We should not end this discussion without pointing out that expansions other than the classical power series expansion employed here are possible. In particular, we should like to mention in passing a certain advantage of using an expansion into the Zernike [2] polynomials which form a complete orthogonal set over a unit circle. By way of a brief summary, one expands $\Delta(\rho, \phi)$ into the form

$$\Delta(\rho, \phi) = \sum_{\substack{n=2 \\ (n, \text{even})}}^{\infty} \frac{a_{no}}{\sqrt{2}} R_n^o(\rho) + \sum_{n=1}^{\infty} \sum_{\substack{m=1 \\ (n-m, \text{even})}}^{\infty} a_{nm} R_n^m(\rho) \cos m\phi,$$

where

$$R_n^m(\rho) = \frac{1}{[(n-m)/2]!\rho^m} \left[\frac{d}{d(\rho^2)} \right]^{(n-m)/2} \{(\rho^2)^{(n+m)/2}(\rho^2 - 1)^{(n-m)/2}\}$$

and

$$\frac{1}{\pi} \int_0^1 \int_0^{2\pi} R_n^m(\rho) R_{n'}^{m'}(\rho) \cos m\phi \cos m'\phi \, \rho \, d\rho \, d\phi = \begin{cases} \dfrac{\delta_{nn'}\delta_{mm'}}{2n+2} \; ; & n \geq 1, \\ \\ 1, & n = 0. \end{cases}$$

Because of this orthogonality condition, the mean square wave-front deformation E_o reduces to

$$E_0 = \sum_{\substack{n=1 \\ (n-m, \text{even})}}^{\infty} \sum_{m=0}^{\infty} \frac{a_{nm}^2}{2n+2},$$

which is the sum of positive, linearly independent terms. Hence, in this form, it is not a question of aberration balancing but merely a reduction of as many of the a_{mn}'s to zero as is possible. For example R_6^0 is given by

$$R_6^0(\rho) = 20 \left(\rho^6 - \tfrac{3}{2}\rho^4 + \tfrac{3}{5}\rho^2 - \frac{1}{20} \right)$$

which, when compared with Eq. (4–18), represents the wave front having the minimum mean square deformation from the mean. In short, each Zernike polynomial is defined in such a way that it possesses that property. To pursue this point further would unfortunately lead us too far astray, and the interested reader is invited to consult the several excellent references on the subject.

References

1. E. H. Linfoot, *Recent Advances in Optics*, Oxford Univ. Press (1958).
2. M. Born and E. Wolf, *Principles of Optics*. Pergamon Press (1959).
3. A. Maréchal and M. Françon, *Editions de la Revue d'Optique*. Paris (1960).
4. H. H. Hopkins, *Wave Theory of Aberrations*. Oxford Univ. Press (1953).

5

Diffraction Theory of Image Formation

5-1 General considerations

Thus far we have considered two widely separated topics; linear filter theory and geometrical optics. We shall now attempt to justify the introduction of these topics by demonstrating how both, in fact, are intimately associated with the concept of image formation in optics as a filtering of spatial frequencies. In our earlier discussion, it was pointed out that the performance of the system was determined from either a knowledge of the system's impulse response (Green's function) or its Fourier transform, which is the frequency response. In optics, the impulse is a point source of light in object space, and the Green's function for the instrument (called the spread function in optical literature) is given by the light intensity distribution in the point image. The optical frequency response is then the two dimensional Fourier transform of this distribution and is called the optical contrast transfer function.

From this point on, we can apply, with minor modifications, the concepts of linear filter theory, which are well established in the field of electric circuitry.

But how does one determine the distribution of light in the point image? With reference to Fig. 5-1, we now symbolize an optical instrument by four planes which are labeled the object plane, entrance pupil, exit pupil, and image plane. Consider an isolated point source at P radiating spherical wavelets, portions of which enter the optical instrument. It is the purpose of the instrument to transform that spherically expanding wave front (surface of constant phase or optical path) into a spherically converging wave front centered on P', which is the Gaussian image of P. In practice, the wave front emerging from the instrument is never quite spherical, and the amount by which it deviates from a reference sphere centered on P' is what we called Δ in the previous chapter. Now certainly there exist very well-corrected systems for which Δ is negligibly small. On the basis of geometrical optics alone, we would be led to the conclusion that for such well-corrected systems, all the rays converge on P' indicating a delta-function-like impulse response and hence an all-pass frequency response.

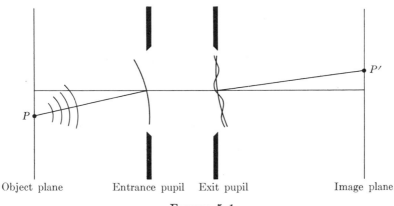

Object plane   Entrance pupil   Exit pupil   Image plane

FIGURE 5–1

But we know from experience that is not the case. There always exists a patch of light called the *diffraction disc* about the image of a point even in the best of instruments. This is not surprising. A star situated at the far edge of our galaxy many light years away sends out informaton concerning its location, uniformly spread over 4π steradians and filling all space. Considering the fraction of that wave front which enters the telescope to the total spherical surface, we do not wonder that there is some uncertainty concerning the precise location of the star from observations made on the patch of light in the focal plane of the telescope.

In short, we need physical optics in the form of Huygens principle to determine the light amplitude, and hence the intensity distribution in the image plane, from a knowledge of the amplitude and phase of the wave disturbance over the exit pupil of the instrument. Does this mean that we banish entirely geometrical optics? Not at all. Temporarily, if we ignore the question of absorption, or coating, that would affect the amplitude of the disturbance over the exit pupil, then we find that the phase of the disturbance is represented precisely by the optical path which is the quantity that the lens designer deals with in passing from surface to surface. Although, in principle, this addition of optical lengths can be carried out to within any accuracy desired up to the exit pupil, it is necessary to use physical optics in passing from the exit pupil to the image plane in order to determine the distribution of light in the point image. The fact that the diagrams of ray intercepts in the previous chapter often roughly correspond to the actual patterns when the wave deviations are several wavelengths or more is an interesting form of an *optical correspondence principle*, but it should not distract us from the more fundamental fact that what happens between the exit pupil of the instrument and the image plane is basically a problem in wave propagation. From this point of view, the optical frequency response should not be looked upon as a *fait accompli;* i.e., something to be measured only after the instrument is designed, produced, and mounted. But rather it is a quantity under the direct control of the lens designer and is perfectly predictable from the shape of the wave front leaving the exit pupil of the instrument.

5–2 Basic diffraction problem

To bring these ideas into sharper focus we now turn our attention to the basic problem in diffraction theory: given the optical disturbance everywhere over a surface surrounding a point Q' (Fig. 5–2) to determine the disturbance at Q'. This is obviously the wave analogue of the standard electrostatic problem.

Here, by the optical disturbance $\phi(x, y, z, t)$, we mean one of the scalar components of the electric vector associated with natural unpolarized light. Since there are no sources inside the region of interest, $\phi(\mathbf{r}, t)$ satisfies the homogeneous wave equation

$$\nabla^2 \phi = \frac{1}{c^2} \frac{\partial^2 \phi}{\partial t^2}.$$ (5–1)

By decomposing $\phi(\mathbf{r}, t)$ into its harmonic components in the form

$$\phi(\mathbf{r}, t) = \frac{1}{2\pi} \int_{-\infty}^{\infty} u_\omega(\mathbf{r}) e^{-i\omega t} \, d\omega$$ (5–2)

and substituting into Eq. (5–1), we have the Helmholtz equation

$$\nabla^2 u_\omega + k^2 u_\omega = 0,$$ (5–3)

where

$$k = \frac{\omega}{c} = \frac{2\pi}{\lambda}$$

is the wave number, and where henceforth we shall omit the subscript on $u(\mathbf{r})$. At any time, we can recover, from Eq. (5–2), the time dependence

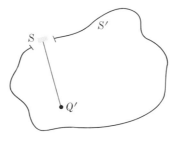

FIGURE 5–2

of the disturbance from a knowledge of $u(\mathbf{r})$. The Green's function for this equation is of the form

$$\nabla^2 G + k^2 G = -\delta(\mathbf{r} - \mathbf{r}'). \tag{5-4}$$

Next, following the method outlined in Chapter 1, we multiply Eq. (5-3) by G, Eq. (5-4) by u, and subtract and integrate over the volume surrounding Q'. The result is

$$\iiint (G\nabla^2 u - u\nabla^2 G)\, d\tau = \iiint u\, \delta(\mathbf{r} - \mathbf{r}')'\, d\tau = 4\pi u(Q').$$

In three dimensions, Green's theorem of vector analysis is the equivalent of the bilinear concomitant of Chapter 1 so that we reduce the volume integral to a surface integral in the form

$$u(Q') = \frac{1}{4\pi} \iint (G\,\mathbf{grad}\, u - u\,\mathbf{grad}\, G) \cdot \mathbf{n}\, da.$$

We shall now attempt to apply this formula directly to the situation depicted in Fig. 5-3, where the surface of integration includes the plane Σ of the exit pupil extended to infinity Σ' and closed by an infinite sphere Σ'' surrounding P'.

We can now show by an order of magnitude argument that the contribution from Σ'' can be made to vanish. Further, using the Kirchhoff boundary condition $u = 0 = \partial u/\partial n$ over the unilluminated plane of the exit pupil Σ', we are left with an integration over Σ in the form

$$u(Q') = \frac{1}{4\pi} \iint_{\Sigma} \left(G\frac{\partial u}{\partial n} - u\frac{\partial G}{\partial n} \right) da. \tag{5-5}$$

Conventionally one would now insert $G = e^{ikr}/r$ as the spherically sym-

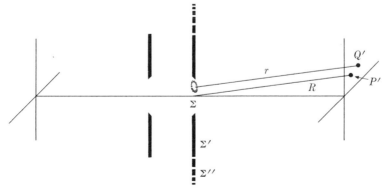

FIGURE 5-3

metric solution of Eq. (5–4), introduce the fact that the aperture itself is illuminated, from behind, by a source point so that $u = e^{ikr_1}/r_1$, and then integrate over $e^{-iwt}(d\omega/2\pi)$ to recover the time dependence. As a result of those manipulations, one ends up with the satisfyingly correct obliquity factor and the celebrated Kirchhoff's theorem which demonstrates that the disturbance at Q' at time t is made up of three contributions: the disturbance over the boundary, its normal derivative, and its time derivative, all of which are evaluated r/c sec in the past. However, the solution is now overdetermined; for if, in fact, we knew the space-time disturbance over the aperture, then, in principle, we would also know the space and time derivatives of the disturbance.

Following Sommerfeld [1], we prefer instead to remove the redundancy by constructing a Green's function that vanishes over the region of integration Σ. This is consistent with the assertions, made in Chapters 1 and 2, concerning the necessity for stating the boundary conditions on the Green's function. If G vanishes over Σ, Eq. (5–5) reduces to

$$u(Q') = -\frac{1}{4\pi} \iint_\Sigma u \frac{\partial G}{\partial n} \, da. \tag{5–6}$$

The problem now is to construct a Green's function G which vanishes over Σ, but whose normal derivative $\partial G/\partial n$ does not vanish on Σ. For a plane surface, as Sommerfeld has shown, the method is reduced to the construction of an image source point quite similar to standard practice, when dealing with electrostatic problems. For our purposes, we construct a Green's function by placing a point source at the observation point Q' and another point source radiating out of phase with this, but located at the geometrical image of Q' at Q_1' which is to the left* of the exit pupil plane as shown in Fig. 5–4. The resulting Green's function now takes the form

$$G = \frac{e^{ikr}}{r} - \frac{e^{ikr_1}}{r_1}$$

which clearly vanishes for $r = r_1$ over the entire plane of the exit pupil

---

* Since we are interested in the optical disturbance to the right of this plane only, any machinations on the left-hand side are "fair game" in order to construct the proper Green's function which, after all, is merely a conventional mathematical tool to help solve the problem. Recall, for instance, the trick of placing a point charge inside a grounded conducting sphere in the presence of an external point charge to construct a field which vanishes over the surface of the sphere. Once again, the step is justified on the grounds that we want to determine the electrostatic field in the region *outside* the sphere. We know the field inside.

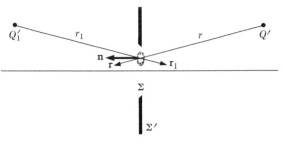

FIGURE 5–4

Σ and Σ', and therefore removes the necessity for having to say anything at all about $\partial u/\partial n$ over this plane.

So far as **grad** G is concerned, however, we have

$$\frac{\partial G}{\partial n} = \frac{e^{ikr}}{r}\left(ik - \frac{1}{r}\right)\cos(\mathbf{r}, \mathbf{n}) - \frac{e^{ikr_1}}{r_1}\left(ik - \frac{1}{r_1}\right)\cos(\mathbf{r_1}, \mathbf{n})$$

which, as $r_1 \to r$ and $\cos(\mathbf{r_1}, \mathbf{n}) \to -\cos(\mathbf{r}, \mathbf{n})$, becomes

$$\frac{\partial G}{\partial n} = 2\frac{e^{ikr}}{r}\left(ik - \frac{1}{r}\right)\cos(\mathbf{r}, \mathbf{n}),$$

and, of course, $G = 0$.

Next we make the perfectly reasonable approximations in visible optics that

$$k = \frac{2\pi}{\lambda} \gg \frac{1}{r} \qquad \text{and} \qquad \cos(\mathbf{r}, \mathbf{n}) \cong 1.$$

Under these conditions, Eq. 5–6 becomes

$$u(Q') = -\frac{ik}{2\pi}\iint_{\Sigma} u\frac{e^{ikr}}{r}\,da, \qquad (5\text{–}7)$$

which directly illustrates the way each surface element $u\,da$ contributes to the disturbance at Q' in the form of a superposition of spherical waves.

5–3 Equations governing image formation

It now remains to describe u over the surface. In keeping with the terminology of the previous chapter, we assign to Q' the coordinates (x, y, o), and, to element da, we assign the coordinates (u, v, w). Clearly, if the instrument succeeded in transforming the incoming wave front to a spherical surface centered on P', then u would have the form e^{-ikR}/R. In general, however, the surface of constant phase will deviate from a sphere by a small factor $\Delta(u, v, h)$, and to allow for amplitude variations due to coating and the like, we write

$$u_\Sigma = |F(u, v)| \frac{e^{-ik(R+\Delta)}}{R} .$$

Now letting $F(u, v) = |F(u, v)|e^{-ik\Delta(u,v)}$ represent the complex amplitude disturbance over the exit pupil, we have

$$u(Q') = \frac{-ike^{-ikR}}{2\pi R} \iint_\Sigma F(u, v) \frac{e^{ikr}}{r} \, da,$$

where

$$
\begin{aligned}
r^2 &= (x - u)^2 + (y - v)^2 + w^2 \\
&= R^2 + x^2 + y^2 - 2(ux + vy).
\end{aligned}
$$

As the contributions from the different elements da add up over the aperture, the term $1/r$ will not change appreciably, yet small changes in r can cause the complex exponential to undergo considerable change. Hence pulling $1/r$ outside the integral and expanding s in the exponent in the series, we get

$$r = R - \frac{(ux + vy)}{R} + \frac{x^2 + y^2}{R} + \cdots \qquad (5\text{–}8)$$

We shall omit now the higher-order terms on the grounds that we are concerned with the light disturbance only in the small region centered about the principal ray. Under these conditions Eq. (5–7) becomes

$$u(x, y) = C \iint_\Sigma F(u, v)e^{-ik/R[(ux+vy)]} \, du \, dv,$$

where the complex constant C has been introduced to absorb all terms not depending on u and v. To cast this expression into a neater form, we introduce first the angular coordinates

$$\mu = \frac{u}{R} ; \qquad \nu = \frac{v}{R} ,$$

then the "reduced" coordinates*

$$\beta = k\mu = \frac{ku}{R} , \qquad \gamma = k\nu = \frac{kv}{R} ;$$

also

$$\alpha^2 = \beta^2 + \gamma^2 = \left(\frac{ka\rho}{R}\right)^2 ; \qquad 0 \le \rho \le 1.$$

---

* Note that β and γ have dimensions of spatial frequencies, radians per length.

Further, we define $F(u, v) = F(\beta, \gamma)$, such that

$$F(\beta, \gamma) = 0 \quad \text{for} \quad \alpha^2 = \beta^2 + \gamma^2 > \frac{k^2 a^2}{R^2} = k^2 \sin^2 \theta.$$

From Eq. (5–8), we then have that except for a constant A, the light disturbance in the Gaussian image plane, due to a point source in object space, is the two-dimensional Fourier transform of the disturbance over the exit pupil in the form

$$u(x, y) = A \int\!\!\int_{-\infty}^{\infty} F(\beta, \gamma) e^{-i(\beta x + \gamma y)} \, d\beta \, d\gamma.$$

For coherent illumination, this is the Green's function for the instrument since it adds linearly from point to point. Conversely, its Fourier transform $F(\beta, \gamma)$ is the frequency response or transfer function for coherent illumination. It is this very fact that makes spatial filtering possible with coherent light, but we will return to this later.

For the more general case of incoherently illuminated or self-luminous objects, $|u(x, y)|^2$ adds linearly and represents the Green's function or "spread function" $s(x, y)$ of the instrument in the form

$$s(x, y) = u(x, y) u^*(x, y).$$

The normalized transfer function for this case now becomes

$$\tau(\boldsymbol{\omega}) = \tau(\omega_x, \omega_y) = \frac{\displaystyle\int\!\!\int_{-\infty}^{\infty} s(x, y) e^{i(\boldsymbol{\omega} \cdot \mathbf{r})} \, dx \, dy}{\displaystyle\int\!\!\int_{-\infty}^{\infty} s(x, y) \, dx \, dy}.$$

Proceeding one step further and invoking the convolution theorem for the transform of a product, we have

$$\tau(\omega_x, \omega_y) = \frac{\displaystyle\int\!\!\int_{-\infty}^{\infty} F(\beta, \gamma) F^*(\beta - \omega_x, \gamma - \omega_y) \, d\beta \, d\gamma}{\displaystyle\int\!\!\int_{-\infty}^{\infty} |F(\beta, \gamma)|^2 \, d\beta \, d\gamma}. \tag{5–9}$$

which is an extremely important result. This result is important for several reasons. First, it describes directly the way in which the wave-front deformation influences the spatial frequency response. Consequently, it allows one to determine this frequency response directly from information

TABLE 5–1

	Two-dimensional: point source; spherical lens; circular aperture	One-dimensional: line source; cylindrical lens; slit aperture
Complex amplitude distribution in the exit pupil	$F(\beta,\gamma) = \lvert F(\beta,\gamma)\rvert e^{-ik\Delta(\beta,\gamma)}, \quad \beta,\gamma \subset \Sigma$ $= 0, \quad \beta,\gamma \not\subset \Sigma$ $\beta = \dfrac{ku}{R}, \quad \gamma = \dfrac{kv}{R}$	$F(\beta) = \lvert F(\beta)\rvert e^{-ik\Delta(\beta)}, \quad \beta \subset \Sigma$ $= 0, \quad \beta \not\subset \Sigma$ $\beta = \dfrac{ku}{R}$
Complex amplitude distribution in the point (line) image	$u(x,y) = A\displaystyle\iint_{-\infty}^{\infty} F(\beta,\gamma)e^{-i(\beta x+\gamma y)}\,d\beta\,d\gamma$	$u(x) = A\displaystyle\int_{-\infty}^{\infty} F(\beta)e^{-i\beta x}\,d\beta$
Intensity spread function	$s(x,y) = \lvert u(x,y)\rvert^2$	$s(x) = \lvert u(x)\rvert^2$
Normalized transfer function	$\tau(\omega_x,\omega_y) = \dfrac{\displaystyle\iint_{-\infty}^{\infty} s(x,y)e^{i\omega\cdot r}\,dx\,dy}{\displaystyle\iint_{-\infty}^{\infty} s(x,y)\,dx\,dy}$ $\tau(\omega_x,\omega_y) = \dfrac{\displaystyle\iint_{-\infty}^{\infty} F(\beta,\gamma)F^*(\beta-\omega_x,\gamma-\omega_y)\,d\beta\,d\gamma}{\displaystyle\iint_{-\infty}^{\infty} \lvert F(\beta,\gamma)\rvert^2\,d\beta\,d\gamma}$	$\tau(\omega_x) = \dfrac{\displaystyle\int_{-\infty}^{\infty} s(x)e^{i\omega_x x}\,dx}{\displaystyle\int_{-\infty}^{\infty} s(x)\,dx}$ $\tau(\omega_x) = \dfrac{\displaystyle\int_{-\infty}^{\infty} F(\beta)F^*(\beta-\omega_x)\,d\beta}{\displaystyle\int_{-\infty}^{\infty} \lvert F(\beta)\rvert^2\,d\beta}$

over the exit pupil without having to examine, in detail, the diffraction pattern which is sometimes very complicated. In addition, although in principle, knowledge of $s(x, y)$ and $\tau(\omega)$ are equivalent, since they are related by a Fourier transformation, the shifting process by which $\tau(\omega)$, in Eq. (5–9), is determined is, in a way, a smoothing operation so that information concerning the quality and performance of the instrument is very often more conveniently gained from a plot of $\tau(\omega)$ than $s(x, y)$. Finally, it should be pointed out that the important relation in Eq. (5–9) came about from two separate and distinct Fourier transformations. The first, between $u(x, y)$ and $F(\beta, \gamma)$, merely describes the fact that, by the use of only Huygen's principle, it is a good approximation in the visible region of the spectrum to treat the far-field or Fraunhofer pattern as the two-dimensional Fourier transform of the aperture distribution. The second Fourier transformation came about by our desire to treat optical image formation as a filtering of spatial frequencies. Consequently, it was only natural to find the impulse response and its mate, the frequency response, through a Fourier transformation.

By way of summary, we now list the more important of these relations in Table 5–1.

5–4 Diffraction by a slit

To close out this section, we shall now attempt to illustrate the use of these formulas for several ideal cases. Consider first an ideal one-dimensional problem for which there is no amplitude variation ($|F(\beta)| = 1$) over a slit of width $d = 2a$ and no aberrations ($\Delta = 0$) are present. Under these conditions, we have

$$u(x) = 2A \int_0^{\beta_0} \cos \beta x \, d\beta,$$

$$u(x) = 2A\beta_0 \left(\frac{\sin \beta_0 x}{\beta_0 x} \right),$$

where $\beta_0 = ka/R$. The normalized spread function is

$$s(x) = \left(\frac{\sin \beta_0 x}{\beta_0 x} \right)^2. \tag{5–10}$$

To determine the transfer function, we can either Fourier transform Eq. (5–10) or perform the convolution shown in Fig. 5–5. Choosing the latter, we have

$$\tau(\omega_x) = \frac{1}{2\beta_0} \int_{\omega_x - \beta_0}^{\beta_0} d\beta = \left(1 - \frac{\omega_x}{2\beta_0} \right), \qquad |\omega_x| \leq 2\beta_0,$$

$$= 0, \qquad\qquad\qquad\qquad\qquad\qquad\qquad |\omega_x| > 2\beta_0.$$

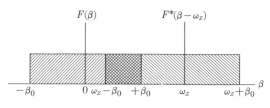

FIGURE 5–5

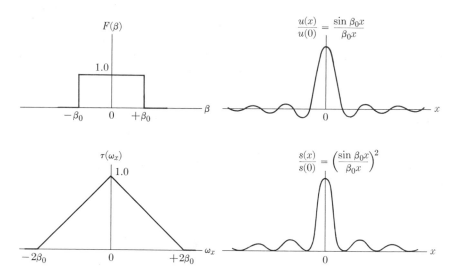

FIGURE 5–6

In terms of the sine wave resolution limit, due to diffraction alone, we have

$$\omega_x = \frac{2\pi}{P_x} = 2\beta_0 = 2k \sin \theta \quad \text{or} \quad \frac{1}{P_x} = \Re_x = \frac{2 \sin \theta}{\lambda},$$

in lines per mm, where $\sin \theta = a/R$ is the semiaperture angle. For an object at infinity $R = f$, the focal length, and $\Re_x = 1/\lambda F^{\#}$, where $F^{\#} = f/d$. As an example, for image formation in green light with $\lambda = 0.5 \, \mu$, the ultimate sine wave resolution due to diffraction is $\Re_x = 2000/F^{\#}$ so that for an $F/5$ system $\Re_x = 400$ lines per mm. Figure 5–6 summarizes the situation for this ideal one-dimensional problem.

5–5 The Michelson stellar interferometer

Next, to emphasize the more important features, we treat the one-dimensional equivalent of the Michelson stellar interferometer (Fig. 5–7). First, we shall calculate the distribution of light intensity in the image of thin line source at a great distance with two thin slits placed in the aper-

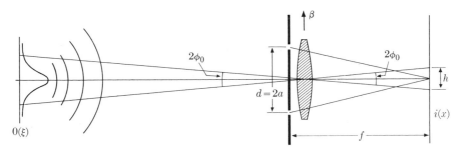

FIGURE 5–7

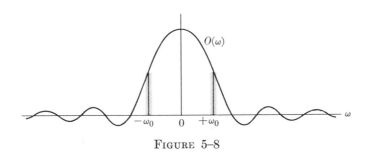

FIGURE 5–8

ture. We represent these slits by $F(\beta) = \delta(\beta \pm \beta_0)$ so that

$$u(x) = 2A \int_0^\infty \delta(\beta - \beta_0) \cos \beta x \, d\beta, \qquad \beta_0 = \frac{ka}{f},$$

$$u(x) = 2A \cos \beta_0 x.$$

The intensity distribution is given by

$$s(x) = 4A^2 \cos^2 \beta_0 x,$$
$$s(x) = 2A^2(1 + \cos 2\beta_0 x).$$

The transfer function is the Fourier transform of the intensity distribution and consists of a d-c term plus spectral components at

$$\omega_0 = \pm 2\beta_0 = \pm kd/f.$$

In terms of the equation relating the object and image spatial spectra (Fig. 5–8),
$$I(\omega) = \tau(\omega)O(\omega),$$

we see that by varying the distance d between slits, we can, in effect, harmonically analyze the structure of the object intensity distribution.

This can be seen in another way by determining the structure of the image in the form

$$i(x) = \int_{-\infty}^{\infty} s(x - \xi) o(\xi) \, d\xi,$$

where

$$s(x - \xi) = 2A^2[1 + \cos \omega_0(x - \xi)]$$
$$= 2A^2[1 + \cos \omega_0\xi \cos \omega_0 x + \sin \omega_0\xi \sin \omega_0 x].$$

We then have

$$i(x) = B_0 + B_c(\omega_0) \cos \omega_0 x + B_s(\omega_0) \sin \omega_0 x,$$

where

$$B_0 = 2A^2 \int_{-\infty}^{\infty} o(\xi) \, d\xi = \text{const},$$

$$B_c(\omega_0) = 2A^2 \int_{-\infty}^{\infty} o(\xi) \cos \omega_0\xi \, d\xi,$$

and

$$B_s(\omega_0) = 2A^2 \int_{-\infty}^{\infty} o(\xi) \sin \omega_0\xi \, d\xi.$$

For simplicity we assume that the object structure is symmetrical* so that $B_s(\omega_0) = 0$, and we have finally

$$i(x) = B_0 + B_c(\omega_0) \cos \omega_0 x.$$

It is interesting to note that the image always appears as a set of cosinusoidal fringes. Even for a single point source, the image in no way resembles the object. We have, in effect, purposely encoded the image and temporarily discarded information concerning the structure of the object. Later, of course, this is the very information we seek to recover by varying the slit separation.

Following Michelson, we define the "visibility" of the fringes as

$$V = V(\omega_0) = \frac{i_{max} - i_{min}}{i_{max} + i_{min}} = \frac{B_c(\omega_0)}{B_0} = \frac{\int_0^{\infty} o(\xi) \cos \omega_0\xi \, d\xi}{\int_0^{\infty} o(\xi) \, d\xi}$$

so that the variation in contrast of the fringes with slit separation is, in effect, a plot of the spatial spectrum of the object from which the object distribution itself can be determined by a Fourier transformation.

---

* Otherwise, we must record not only the amplitude but the phase (location of the fringes) to reconstruct the object distribution.

Consider a uniformly bright object whose geometrical image subtends an angle $2\phi_0 = h/f$ in the image plane. Then (Fig. 5–9)

$$V(d) = \frac{\sin \omega_0 h/2}{\omega_0 h/2},$$

where

$$\frac{\omega_0 h}{2} = \frac{k \, d \, h}{2f} = k\phi_0 d,$$

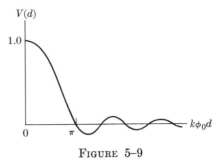

FIGURE 5–9

which indicates that the slit separation at which the fringe contrast first passes through a phase reversal is given by $d = \pi/k\phi_0$. Conversely, by noting the slit separation* at which this occurs, we can determine the angular size of the object in the form

$$2\phi_0 = \frac{\lambda}{d}.$$

5–6 Diffraction by a circular aperture

Finally, we turn to a case of particular interest, that of image formation by an ideal lens of radius a. Here, because of inherent rotational symmetry, we have

$$u(r) = 2\pi A \int_0^\infty F(\alpha) J_0(\alpha r) \alpha \, d\alpha.$$

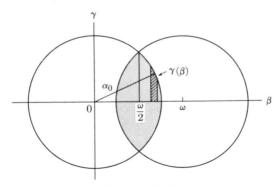

FIGURE 5–10

* It should be added that in order to amplify the phase difference [2] at the two slits, Michelson mounted two mirrors on a long girder and redirected the light to the slits using two inner mirrors. For the star Betelgeuse of angular diameter 0.047″, the outer mirrors were 121″ apart.

In the ideal case $F(\alpha) = 1$ for $0 \leq \alpha \leq \alpha_0$ and zero elsewhere so that the normalized intensity pattern is given by

$$\frac{s(r)}{s(0)} = \left[2 \frac{J_1(\alpha_0 r)}{\alpha_0 r} \right]^2, \qquad \alpha_0 = \frac{ka}{R},$$

which is the celebrated Airy diffraction disc.

The transfer function possesses rotational symmetry also, and hence, for convenience, we shall calculate the convolution integral for a shift in the β-direction (Fig. 5–10):

$$\tau(\omega) = \frac{4 \int_{\omega/2}^{\alpha_0} \gamma(\beta) \, d\beta}{\int_0^{\alpha_0} \int_0^{2\pi} \alpha \, d\alpha \, d\phi} = \frac{4}{\pi \alpha_0^2} \int_{\omega/2}^{\alpha_0} \sqrt{\alpha_0^2 - \beta^2} \, d\beta,$$

or

$$\tau(\omega) = \frac{2}{\pi} \left[\cos^{-1} \frac{\omega}{2\alpha_0} - \frac{\omega}{2\alpha_0} \sqrt{1 - \left(\frac{\omega}{2\alpha_0} \right)^2} \right] \qquad 0 \leq \frac{\omega}{2\alpha_0} \leq 1,$$

$$= 0, \qquad\qquad\qquad\qquad\qquad\qquad\qquad \left| \frac{\omega}{2\alpha_0} \right| > 1.$$

Figure 5–11 summarizes the results of this section.

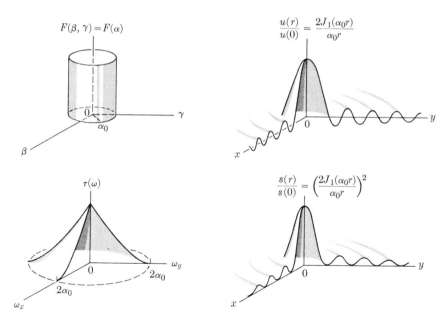

FIGURE 5–11

By way of summary then, we have succeeded in describing the way in which the amplitude and phase over the exit pupil influences the transfer function of an optical system, and, in the process, we have illustrated its behavior in several ideal cases. In the next chapter, we will investigate the more interesting and more practical problems of first finding the effects of arbitrary amplitude and phase (aberrations) variations on the transfer function (the analysis problem) and later investigate the possibility of altering the aperture distribution to achieve some prespecified end (the synthesis problem). We point out here that from the form of Eq. (5–9), every optical system employing incoherent illumination is basically a *low-pass* spatial frequency filter whose ultimate resolution is set solely by the wavelength and numerical aperture.

References

1. A. SOMMERFELD, *Lectures in Theoretical Physics.* Vol. 4. *Optics.* Academic Press (1954).

2. W. E. WILLIAMS, *Applications of Interferometry.* Methuen (1954).

3. A. MARÉCHAL and M. FRANÇON, *Editions de la Revue d'Optique.* Paris (1960).

6

Analysis and Synthesis

6-1 General considerations

We have seen in the previous chapter that the amplitude and phase over the exit pupil of an optical instrument determines its performance both in terms of the impulse response, or spread function, and its Fourier transform, the transfer function. Further, we point out for emphasis that although it is becoming common practice in the optical industry to measure the transfer function for finished lens systems, it is also perfectly feasible to calculate this function during the design stages, with quantities intimately related to those with which the lens designer is ordinarily concerned. In fact, it is desirable to direct the progress of the design by examining from time to time the behavior of the transfer function at several focal settings and field angles, and in different colors.

Using the set of equations in Table 5–1, we will proceed, in this chapter, to illustrate the effect of amplitude and phase variations over the aperture on the transfer function both for the one-dimensional and the two-dimensional cases. Before that, however, we should like to draw some general conclusions. Consider first Schwarz's inequality [1]

$$\left| \int f^*(x)g(x)\,dx \right|^2 \leq \int f^*(x)f(x)\,dx \int g^*(x)g(x)\,dx.$$

Applying this directly to the convolution integral for the transfer function of a system with phase variation (aberrations) only, $|F|^2 = 1$, we have

$$\left| \iint_{-\infty}^{+\infty} F(\beta, \gamma)F^*(\beta - \omega_x, \gamma - \omega_y)\,d\beta\,d\gamma \right| \leq \iint_{-\infty}^{+\infty} d\beta\,d\gamma$$

or

$$|\tau(\omega)| \leq \tau_0(\omega),$$

with the subscript 0 referring to the ideal case of unit amplitude and zero phase over the exit pupil. In other words, excluding for the moment amplitude variations, the effect of aberrations alone is to produce always a loss in the contrast transfer function at all frequencies. On the other hand, for pure amplitude variations $F = F^*$, produced perhaps by coating, it is clear that because of the way in which we have agreed to normalize $\tau(0) = 1$, there are certain regions in frequency space for which $\tau(\omega)$ can exceed $\tau_0(\omega)$, where

$$\tau(\omega) = \frac{\displaystyle\iint_{-\infty}^{+\infty} F(\beta, \gamma)F(\beta - \omega_x, \gamma - \omega_y)\, d\beta\, d\gamma}{\displaystyle\iint_{-\infty}^{+\infty} F^2(\beta, \gamma)\, d\beta\, d\gamma}.$$

For photographic purposes, one must pay for this increased contrast with a longer exposure time. As we shall see later in the illustrations and from intuition, coatings which weigh against the central portion of the aperture yield an increase in contrast for the fine detail, and those which taper the amplitude toward the edge of the aperture result in higher contrast for the coarse detail.

6–2 Small aberrations

Let us return now to the case of pure phase variations. A quantity of considerable interest in classical optics is the Strehl [2] definition $\mathfrak{D}$, which is defined as the ratio of the light intensity at the maximum of the diffraction pattern to that of the same instrument without aberrations. That is,

$$\mathfrak{D} = \frac{s(0, 0)}{s_0(0, 0)} = \left| \iint_a e^{-ik\Delta(\beta, \gamma)} \frac{d\beta\, d\gamma}{a} \right|^2,$$

where $a = \iint d\beta\, d\gamma$ is the area of the aperture in the reduced coordinates. As Maréchal [3] has shown, an interesting inequality can be obtained by using $\Delta''(\beta, \gamma)$, the aberration function about the mean reference, as defined in Chapter 4, in place of $\Delta(\beta, \gamma)$. We can then write

$$\mathfrak{D} = \left[\iint_a \cos k\Delta'' \frac{d\beta\, d\gamma}{a} \right]^2 + \left[\iint_a \sin k\Delta'' \frac{d\beta\, d\gamma}{a} \right]^2$$

$$\geq \left[\iint_a \cos k\Delta'' \frac{d\beta\, d\gamma}{a} \right]^2.$$

For small aberrations, we have

$$\mathfrak{D} \geq \left(\iint_a \left[1 - \frac{k^2}{2} \Delta''^2 \right] \frac{d\beta\, d\gamma}{a} \right)^2,$$

where, from Chapter 4,

$$E_0 = \overline{(\Delta'')^2} = \frac{1}{a} \iint_a (\Delta'')^2 \, d\beta \, d\gamma$$

is a quantity previously defined solely from geometrical considerations. The main significance of Maréchal's contribution is that a quantity determined entirely by geometrical averaging (E_0) is intimately related to a classical tolerance factor ($\mathfrak{D}$) defined on the basis of physical optics. The relation between these is

$$\mathfrak{D} \geq \left(1 - \frac{2\pi^2}{\lambda^2} E_0\right)^2.$$

The classical tolerance of $\mathfrak{D} \geq 0.80$* corresponds here to the Maréchal value $E_0 \leq \lambda^2/184$, or in terms of the rms wave-front error,

$$\sqrt{E_0} \leq \frac{\lambda}{13.5}.$$

Identifying E_0 in this equation with $(E_0)_{\min}$ in Eq. (4–22), we are able to nail down to a number the range of focal settings and field angles within which the Maréchal tolerance can be satisfied. For further details on the effect of imposing this tolerance on focal adjustments and aberrations, the interested reader should consult Maréchal's thesis [4] or the excellent book by Maréchal and Françon [5]. By way of illustration, we merely point out here that, assuming the optimum ratio of third- to fifth-order spherical aberration $c_1/d_1 = -\frac{3}{2}$ and the optimum focal setting $\mu = -\delta f/\delta L_{\max} = 0.80$, we can just about reach the Maréchal tolerance for $d_1 \cong 4\lambda$. Of course, for d_1 less than four wavelengths, there is a range of corrections and focal settings for which we can get under the tolerance. The whole situation is summarized in Fig. 6–1.

We should not leave this discussion without pointing out that since $s(x, y)$ and $\tau(\omega)$ are Fourier transform pairs, the Strehl definition can also be defined in frequency space as the normalized volume under the transfer function, in the form

$$\mathfrak{D} = \frac{\displaystyle\iint_{-\infty}^{+\infty} \tau(\omega) \, d\omega_x \, d\omega_y}{\displaystyle\iint_{-\infty}^{+\infty} \tau_0(\omega) \, d\omega_x \, d\omega_y}. \tag{6–1}$$

---

* In the language of antenna theory [3], this corresponds to about 1 db loss in gain due to aberrations through the relation $G = 10 \log_{10}(1/\mathfrak{D})$.

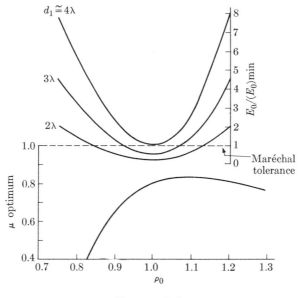

FIGURE 6–1

As Linfoot [6] has pointed out, a direct extension of the statistical descriptions in Chapter 2 to two dimensions shows that for random object scenes with a statistical spectrum, flat up to the cut-off of the filter, the right-hand side of Eq. (6–1) describes the extent to which the peaks and troughs of the image are correlated with the corresponding peaks and troughs of the object distribution.

6–3 Amplitude and phase variation in one dimension

In this section we will illustrate the way in which the form of $F(\beta)$ affects $\tau(\omega_x)$. Consider the tapered aperture distribution shown in Fig. 6–2(a). Substituting this expression into

$$\tau(\omega_x) = \frac{\int_{-\infty}^{+\infty} F(\beta)F^*(\beta - \omega_x)\,d\beta}{\int_{-\infty}^{+\infty} |F(\beta)|^2\,d\beta} \tag{6–2}$$

and carrying out the elementary integration, we get the curves shown in Fig. 6–2(b). Here we see an increase in contrast for the low-frequency end of the curve with a corresponding loss in contrast at the high-frequency end. Conversely, an aperture distribution, such as that shown in Fig. 6–3(a), has just the reverse effect. Figure 6–3(b) exhibits the way in which the contrast has been increased for the fine detail by weighing against

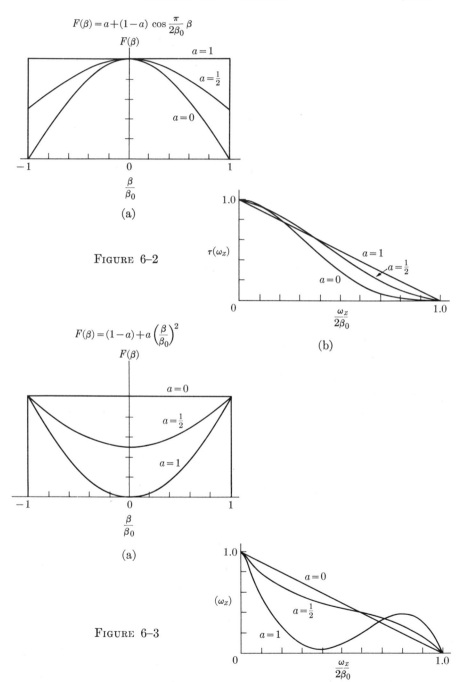

$$F(\beta) = a + (1-a)\,\cos\frac{\pi}{2\beta_0}\beta$$

FIGURE 6-2

$$F(\beta) = (1-a) + a\left(\frac{\beta}{\beta_0}\right)^2$$

FIGURE 6-3

the central portion of the aperture. Once again, we repeat for emphasis that these curves are shown on a normalized scale and do not show the loss of total illumination produced by the coating.

Turning now to phase variations, it is easy to see that for $F(\beta) = e^{-ik\,\Delta(\beta)}$, a phase error of the form $\Delta(\beta) = a_n\beta^n$ produces an integrand, in Eq. (6–2), of the form

$$F(\beta)F^*(\beta - \omega_x) = e^{+ikw(\beta,\omega_x)} \tag{6–3}$$

where $w = \Delta(\beta) - \Delta(\beta - \omega_x)$ is a polynomial of degree $n - 1$ in β. Let us now analyze the sequence of curves shown in Figs. 6–4(a) through 6–4(f)* which illustrate, for $n = 0, 1, 2, 3, 4$, the effect of phase error on the transfer function:

1. $n = 0$. As we should expect, the appearance of a constant in the phase function merely reflects the choice of a different reference sphere and hence has no effect on either the results of geometrical or physical optics.

2. $n = 1$. After subtraction, the dependence of the right-hand side of Eq. (6–3) on β disappears, leaving only a linear term in ω_x. It is well known in communication theory that a linear phase shift has only the effect of shifting the impulse response as a unit. Thus, in optics, the insertion of a glass wedge merely shifts the entire image as a unit. On the other hand, the aberration known as distortion is linear in β; the reason that it is harmful, however, is its simultaneous dependence on the cube of the field angle.

3. $n = 2$. This term represents a focusing error. Because of its relative simplicity we shall carry out the integration in detail to show how one calculates curves of this form. Let us assume that we start off with an ideal cylindrical lens $\Delta = 0$ and seek to determine what happens to the transfer function as we move out of focus and introduce a phase error $\Delta(\beta) = b_1(\beta/\beta_0)^2$. Substituting into Eq. (6–2), we have

$$\tau(\omega_x) = \frac{1}{2\beta_0} \int_{\omega_x-\beta_0}^{\beta_0} \exp\frac{-ikb_1}{\beta_0^2}(2\beta\omega_x - \omega_x^2)\, d\beta.$$

Now shifting the coordinate system to the center of the overlapping region $\sigma = \beta - (\omega_x/2)$ and recognizing that the real part of the integrand is an even function, we get

$$\tau(\omega_x) = \frac{1}{\beta_0} \int_0^{\beta_0-(\omega_x/2)} \cos\left(\frac{2kb_1\omega_x}{\beta_0^2}\sigma\right) d\sigma.$$

---

* The reader should be cautioned that h, the field height, has been absorbed into the aberration coefficients in Figs. 6–4 and 6–5.

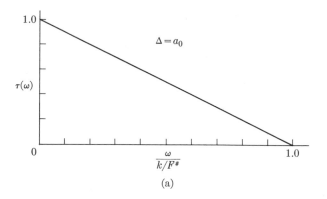

(a)

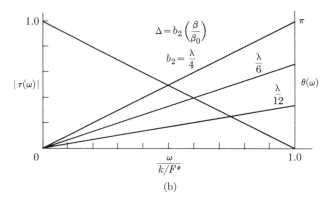

(b)

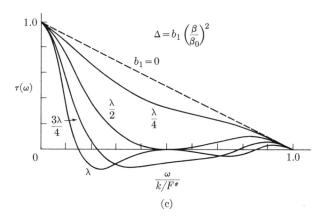

(c)

FIGURE 6–4

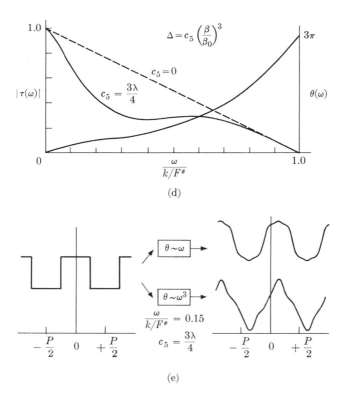

(d)

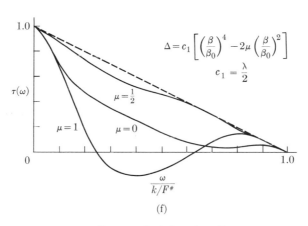

(e)

(f)

FIGURE 6–4 (continued)

Carrying out the integration, we have finally

$$\tau(\omega_x) = \left(1 - \frac{\omega_x}{2\beta_0}\right) \operatorname{sinc}\left[4kb_1 \frac{\omega_x}{2\beta_0}\left(1 - \frac{\omega_x}{2\beta_0}\right)\right], \qquad |\omega_x| \leq 2\beta_0$$

$$= 0, \qquad |\omega_x| > 2\beta_0,$$

where

$$\operatorname{sinc} x = \frac{\sin x}{x}$$

$$2\beta_0 = \frac{k(2a)}{f} = \frac{k}{F\#}$$

$$2a = \text{aperture width.}$$

It is interesting to note, from Fig. 6–4(c), how rapidly the contrast falls off once the Rayleigh tolerance $b_1 = \lambda/4$ has been exceeded. Further, for $b_1 > 2\lambda$, the transfer function behaves like sinc (ωd), which is precisely what we would get if we ignored diffraction effects and assumed from purely geometrical considerations that the light was uniformly spread over a patch of width $2d$ in the out-of-focus plane.

4. $n = 3$. Since the wave front is cubic in β, Fresnel integrals occur in the evaluations of $\tau(\omega_x)$. In addition, it is convenient to cast the transfer function into the form

$$\tau(\omega_x) = \tau_c(\omega_x) + i\tau_s(\omega_x) = |\tau(\omega_x)|e^{i\phi(\omega_x)}$$

where

$$\tau(\omega_x) = \sqrt{\tau_c^2(\omega_x) + \tau_s^2(\omega_x)},$$

$$\phi(\omega_x) = \tan^{-1} \frac{\tau_s(\omega_x)}{\tau_c(\omega_x)},$$

and

$$\tau_c(\omega_x) = \frac{1}{2\beta_0} \int_{\omega_x-\beta_0}^{\beta_0} \cos k \left[\Delta(\beta) - \Delta(\beta - \omega_x)\right] d\beta,$$

$$\tau_s(\omega_x) = \frac{1}{2\beta_0} \int_{\omega_x-\beta_0}^{\beta_0} \sin k \left[\Delta(\beta) - \Delta(\beta - \omega_x)\right] d\beta.$$

A typical curve is shown in Fig. 6–4(d). The effect of the nonlinear phase shift should not be ignored. In Fig. 6–4(e) the image distribution is shown for two systems which have the same amplitude attenuation, but the first has a linear phase shift and the second the phase shift shown in Fig. 6–4(d). In the first case, a viewer would probably have surmised that the object was a square-wave test chart; in the second he might have been misled, due to the fact that the Fourier harmonics did not add up in phase. This is the type of phase error associated with coma.

5. $n = 4$. We end this discussion with curves illustrating the effect of fourth-power phase errors (spherical aberration) in one dimension. For the sake of generality, we have included also a focusing term in Δ. As Fig. 6-4(f) shows, for a half wave of third-order spherical aberration, the best focus for all frequencies lies midway between the marginal and paraxial foci. For larger aberrations, the curves become scrambled and the determination of the "best focus" depends, among other things, upon the structure of the objects and the use to which the instrument is put.

6-4 Amplitude and phase variation in two dimensions

Aside from increased computational difficulties, the situation in two dimensions is not essentially different from that of one-dimensional variations. The sequence of curves in Fig. 6-5* illustrates the effect of the various Seidel aberrations on the transfer function. For the details of the computation in each case, the reader should consult the original literature. Of particular interest is the fact that coma introduces a nonlinear phase shift and that, for astigmatism at the so-called "circle of least confusion," the transfer function is different for line structures having different orientations. In Fig. 6-6, we show how the transfer function varies with the state of correction (ρ_0) and focal setting (μ) when both third- and fifth-order spherical aberrations are present. Clearly, for small aberrations $d_1 \leq 4\lambda$, the Maréchal tolerance yields an unambiguous answer. For larger aberrations, as we shall see, the position of the optimum focal plane depends upon the quality factor invoked to determine it.

We cite the original literature for the more general cases of combinations of aberrations. First, for small aberrations, Maréchal [3] and Steel [9] have published a valuable set of tables that include clear and obstructed apertures. With larger aberrations, and particularly with the conditions under which one may make geometrical approximations, the reader should consult the works of Miyamoto [10] and H. H. Hopkins [11]. In particular, Hopkins has extended the notion of aberration tolerances and has demonstrated a computational scheme for calculating the transfer function when all aberrations are present.

So far as amplitude variations over the exit pupil are concerned, there is an extensive French literature [12] available on methods of "apodization," that is, methods of coating an aperture to achieve some prespecified form for the diffraction pattern. Along these same lines, Luneberg [13] and, more recently, Barakat [14] have attacked the problem of amplitude coating using the variational calculus. In the Luneberg-Barakat scheme, for a given flux through the aperture, one attempts to keep the central maximum of the diffraction pattern as high as possible while imposing some

---

* Part (b) is from Ref. 7, (c) and (d) is from Ref. 8, and (e) is from Ref. 19.

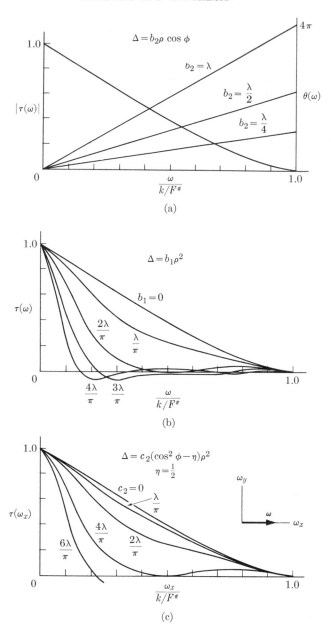

FIGURE 6–5

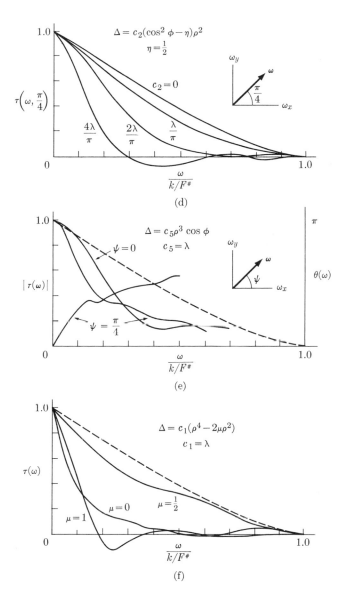

FIGURE 6–5 (*continued*)

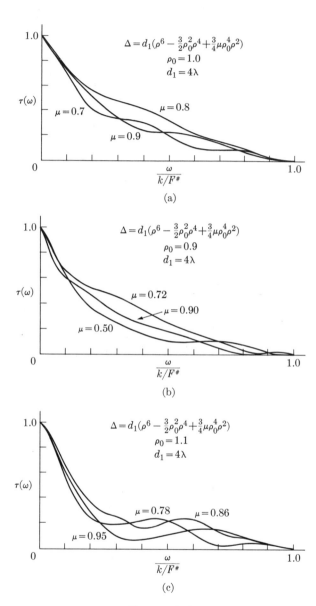

FIGURE 6–6

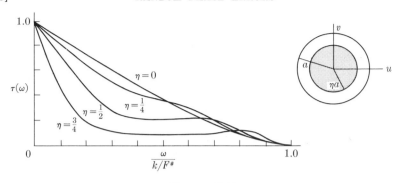

FIGURE 6-7

auxiliary constraint on the pattern. For example, we could demand that the first zero in the pattern move inward to some specified radius smaller than the Airy radius. Or, better yet, we might try to determine the aperture distribution that will concentrate the maximum amount of light in a given area of prespecified radius. These and similar problems have been solved and have interesting interpretations from the communication-theoretic point of view. That amplitude variation which corresponds to a central obstruction is of considerable interest [9, 15]. The problem of determining the transfer function for this case can be reduced to the elementary geometrical problem of calculating the common area of two annuli, as one slides over the other. The result is shown in Fig. 6-7. Again we see an increase in contrast at the high-frequency end of the curve. The curves are in complete harmony with Steward's remarks [16] concerning the narrowing of the central peak and increased two-point resolution with a central obstruction. It is also instructive to point out in passing that for η approaching, but just less than, unity, the curve reduces to peaks at $\omega_x = 0$, $\pm 2\beta_0$. However, this is just what we should expect since the thin annular ring is the two-dimensional, rotationally symmetric equivalent of the double slit in the Michelson stellar interferometer.

6–5 Random phase errors

Let us suppose now that the wave front emerging from an optical instrument exhibits two forms of deviations from a mean reference sphere: the first, $\Delta_c(\beta, \gamma)$, a "controlled" part due to aberrations, and the second, $\Delta_R(\beta, \gamma)$, a "random" part due perhaps to polishing errors or atmospheric effects. Further, if Δ_R is time dependent, causing the diffraction pattern to dance about, then we shall conceptually construct a whole ensemble of identical systems, which may exhibit different point-by-point behavior for $\Delta_R(\beta, \gamma)$ but which are statistically equivalent. Lastly, we assume that we can construct our ensemble in such a way that we can replace time averages by ensemble averages. We now wish to determine,

$$\overline{\tau(\omega)} = K \iint\limits_{-\infty}^{+\infty} \exp\left\{ik[\,\Delta(\beta, \gamma) - \Delta(\beta - \omega_x, \gamma - \omega_y)]\right\}\,d\beta\,d\gamma,$$

where the normalization has been absorbed into K and where $\Delta = \Delta_R + \Delta_C$. The averaging process affects only Δ_R and the result, being independent of β and γ, can be pulled outside the integral. That which is left over is just $\tau_L(\omega)$ the transfer function due to the lens alone. Therefore, writing

$$\overline{\tau(\omega)} = \tau_R(\omega)\tau_L(\omega), \tag{6-4}$$

we must now determine

$$\tau_R(\omega) = \overline{\exp\left\{ik[\,\Delta_R(\beta, \gamma) - \Delta_R(\beta - \omega_x, \gamma - \omega_y)]\right\}}. \tag{6-5}$$

In order to proceed, we must make some assumptions concerning the statistical behavior of $\Delta_R(\beta, \gamma)$. We take as a starting point that $\Delta_R(\beta, \gamma)$ is Gaussianly distributed, has zero mean, variance σ^2, and an autocorrelation function of the form

$$\phi(\omega_x, \omega_y) = \overline{\Delta_R(\beta, \gamma)\,\Delta_R(\beta - \omega_x, \gamma - \omega_y)}.$$

Next we expand the right-hand side of Eq. 6–5 into a series and average term by term to get

$$\tau_R(\omega) = \sum_{n=0}^{\infty} \frac{(ik)^n}{n!}\,\overline{[\,\Delta_R(\beta, \gamma) - \Delta_R(\beta - \omega_x, \gamma - \omega_y)]^n}. \tag{6-6}$$

However, it is the property of a Gaussian variate that the higher-order moments are determined from the first two moments, according to the well-known result [20],

$$\overline{x_1 x_2 x_3 \ldots x_{2p}} = \sum_{\substack{\text{all} \\ \text{pairs}}} \overline{x_i x_j} \ldots \overline{x_k x_l} \ldots \overline{x_m x_n},$$

$$\overline{x_1 x_2 x_3 \ldots x_{2p+1}} = 0.$$

From this property it follows, by induction, that

$$\overline{[\,\Delta_R(\beta, \gamma) - \Delta_R(\beta - \omega_x, \gamma - \omega_y)]^n} = \frac{n!}{(n/2)!}\,[\sigma^2 - \phi(\omega)]^{n/2}, \qquad n \text{ even},$$

$$= 0, \qquad\qquad\qquad n \text{ odd}.$$

Substituting this back into Eq. (6–6) and changing the summation index from n to $j = n/2$, we have

$$\tau_R(\omega) = \sum_{j=0}^{\infty} \frac{\{-k^2[\sigma^2 - \phi(\omega)]\}^j}{j!},$$

which is just the series expansion of the function

$$\tau_R(\omega) = e^{-k^2[\sigma^2 - \phi(\omega)]}.$$

Thus the rate at which the contrast falls off is determined by the mean square of the random fluctuations and the extent to which they are correlated over the aperture, both expressed in wavelength units. In addition, from Eq. (6–4) these random fluctuations can be treated as a linear link in the chain and always result in a loss in contrast and resolution. The ultimate resolution is set by the wavelength and numerical aperture through the term $\tau_L(\omega)$.

6–6 The synthesis problem, coherent illumination

We have, up to this point, confined our attention to optical systems employing incoherent illumination; that is, systems for which the time-averaged square of the electric vector adds linearly from point to point in the image plane. This lack of destructive interference causes such systems to behave always as low-pass filters of spatial frequencies. In order to achieve as much flexibility as exists in electrical filtering, it is necessary to allow both destructive and constructive interference; in short, one must be able to control the amplitude and phase of the point image distribution.

As Maréchal and Croce [17], and O'Neill [18] have shown, this is possible by employing coherent illumination over the object plane. With reference to Fig. 6–8, a Fourier transformation of the transparent object structure takes place as the light passes from the object plane to the filter plane. From Abbé's principle, these Fourier orders are recombined by the second-lens system to form an image. One must bear in mind that in this diagram the optical system to the left of the object system is merely used to illuminate the object plane coherently. One can think of image formation in this system as the result of two successive Fourier transformations. The image is never perfect, however, since the very fine details in the object structure produce Fourier spectra that fall outside the lens aperture. The important point to note is that since the Fourier spectrum of the object is spread over the filter plane, it is possible to control the Fourier orders which constitute the image by inserting the appropriate masks. Perhaps the best known illustration of this effect is the phase-contrast

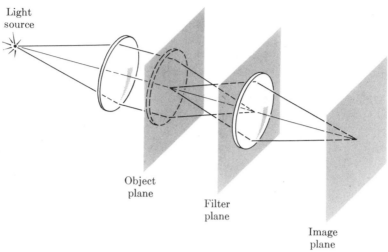

FIGURE 6–8

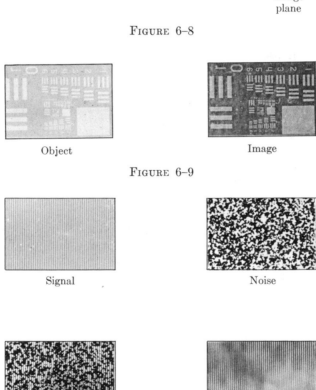

FIGURE 6–10

method, which introduces a phase difference between the direct and diffracted light in order to make visible small phase changes in otherwise indiscernible microscope specimens.

From a communication-theoretic point of view, it is quite easy to demonstrate the "filtering" qualities of this system. Figure 6-9 shows the effect of inserting a small absorbing spot in the filter plane in order to attenuate the background (dc) light with respect to the diffracted (ac) light. The result is an increase in contrast in the image of the resolution chart. In Fig. 6-10, the low-contrast periodic chart was placed together with the optical "noise" in the object plane. A "Dirac comb filter" was then constructed by piercing an opaque mask with a pin at points corresponding to the Fourier spectra of the low-constrast grating. The resulting image shows the effect of blocking out the two-dimensional "noise" spectrum. (Other examples can be cited.) Methods exist for constructing equalizing filters, matched filters, filters to diminish graininess, sharpen edges, etc. A number of optical processing devices [19] using this principle have been developed successfully.

In many cases, one can perform certain operations more easily using optical filters than their electrical counterparts. Maréchal [5] and his co-workers have demonstrated how far one can go in recovering detail from a poor quality photograph by carefully controlling the amplitude and phase of the filtering mask. In principle, all the techniques developed in electric circuit theory can be carried over into optics. The simplification in optics enters by virtue of the fact that separation of the spectra comes about naturally through the very process of diffraction.

References

1. H. Margenau and G. M. Murphy, *The Mathematics of Physics and Chemistry*. D. Van Nostrand (1956).

2. M. Born and E. Wolf, *Principles of Optics*. Pergamon Press (1959).

3. J. Brown, *Microwave Lenses*. Methuen (1953).

4. A. Maréchal, *Editions de la Revue d'Optique*. Paris (1948).

5. A. Maréchal and M. Françon, *Editions de la Revue d'Optique*. Paris (1960).

6. E. H. Linfoot, *J. Opt. Soc. Am.* **46,** 740 (1957).

7. H. H. Hopkins, *Proc. Roy. Soc. London* **A321,** 91 (1955).

8. De, M., *Proc. Roy. Soc. London* **A233,** 91 (1955).

9. W. H. Steel, *Editions de la Revue d'Optique*. Paris (1953).

10. K. Miyamoto, *Progress in Optics*. Vol. 1. E. Wolf, editor. North-Holland (1961).

11. H. H. Hopkins, *Proc. Phys. Soc.* (London) **B70,** 1002 (1957).

12. B. Dossier, *Editions de la Revue d'Optique*. Paris (1954).

13. R. K. LUNEBERG, *Mathematical Theory of Optics* (Lecture notes). Brown University (1944).

14. R. BARAKAT, *J. Opt. Soc. Am.* **52,** 264 (1952).

15. E. L. O'NEILL, *J. Opt. Soc. Am.* **46,** 285 (1956).

16. G. C. STEWARD, *The Symmetrical Optical System.* Cambridge Tract (1928).

17. A. MARÉCHAL and P. CROCE, *Compt. Rend.* **237,** 706 (1953).

18. E. L. O'NEILL, *I. R. E. Trans.-P. G. I. T.* **2,** 56 (1956).

19. A. S. MARATHAY, *Proc. Phys. Soc.* **74,** 721 (1959).

20. M. C. WANG and G. E. UHLENBECK, *Revs. Modern Phys.* **17,** 332 (1945).

21. L. J. CUTRONA, E. N. LEITH, C. J. PALERMO and L. J. PORCELLO *I. R. E. Trans.-P. G. I. T.* **6,** 386 (1960).

7

Statistical Methods

7-1 Random scenes

We have attempted so far to emphasize that there are advantages of conceptual economy in treating image forming instruments as filters of spatial frequencies. In such a treatment the application to periodic object structures or objects consisting of simple geometrical shapes on a dark background is straightforward by Fourier decomposition. For certain applications, as we have seen in the last chapter, one can even consider synthesis methods. However, image formation is often at best a statistical problem. Optical instruments are designed not for any single object structure but for whole classes of objects. Anyone who has ever tried to focus accurately an optical device realizes that the focal setting for maximum contrast in the coarse detail does not necessarily yield maximum contrast for the fine detail. In turning the focusing screw, the viewer is in fact "tuning" to those details in the scene that interest him. We now raise the question: given the contrast transfer function for several focal settings and field angles, how does one select the optimum? Clearly the answer to this question depends at least upon whatever *a priori* information we have concerning the object and the use to which the instrument is to be put. As we will see, demanding maximum sharpness in the image is quite another thing from demanding maximum alignment between the fluctuations of the object and image structures.

We have already used one quality factor from classical optics, the Strehl definition $\mathfrak{D}$. Let us review briefly how this term appears in image formation. According to Lord Rayleigh appreciable deterioration of the image will not occur if the maximum wave deformation from a reference sphere does not exceed $\lambda/4$. Maréchal, on the other hand, examining the whole complex wave front emerging from the exit pupil demonstrated a relation between the root mean square wave-front deformation and the central intensity of the diffraction pattern. Demanding that the ratio of this central intensity to that of the same instrument without aberration exceed 0.8 is equivalent in Maréchal's terms to placing a $\lambda/13.5$ tolerance

on the rms wave-front error. As we have shown, this normalized ratio is
known as the Strehl definition, and in our language it can be written as

$$\mathfrak{D} = \frac{s(0, 0)}{s_0(0, 0)} = \frac{\displaystyle\iint_{-\infty}^{+\infty} \tau(\boldsymbol{\omega}) \, d\boldsymbol{\omega}}{\displaystyle\iint_{-\infty}^{+\infty} \tau_0(\boldsymbol{\omega}) \, d\boldsymbol{\omega}} \, .$$

More recently, Linfoot [1] has suggested quality factors for rating
optical systems which are two-dimensional generalizations of the statistical
descriptions used for linear time filters in Chapter 2. By way of summary,
Linfoot introduced the following factors:

(a) *Relative structural content:*

$$T = \frac{\overline{i^2(x, y)}}{\overline{o^2(x, y)}} \, .$$

The emphasis here is on sharpness through the mean* square criterion.
There is no demand that the peaks and troughs of the object and image
planes are aligned; that is, that the image "look like" the object.

(b) *Correlation quality:*

$$Q = \frac{\overline{i(x, y)o(x, y)}}{\overline{o^2(x, y)}} \, .$$

Here emphasis is on alignment; such a criterion will not, in general, yield
the sharpest image.

(c) *Fidelity defect:*

$$F = 1 - D,$$

where

$$D = \frac{\overline{[o(x, y) - i(x, y)]^2}}{\overline{o^2(x, y)}} \, .$$

As pointed out in Chapter 2, this factor is not independent of the other
two. The three in fact are related through the equation

$$Q = \tfrac{1}{2}(T + F).$$

In this respect F (or D) contains features implied in both Q and T.

---

* The bar here signifies an average taken over a large area.

These factors become more useful when transformed into frequency space in the form:

$$
T = \frac{\displaystyle\iint_{-\infty}^{+\infty} |\tau(\omega)|^2 \Phi_{oo}(\omega)\,d\omega}{\displaystyle\iint_{-\infty}^{+\infty} \Phi_{oo}(\omega)\,d\omega}, \qquad
Q = \frac{\displaystyle\iint_{-\infty}^{+\infty} \tau(\omega)\Phi_{oo}(\omega)\,d\omega}{\displaystyle\iint_{-\infty}^{+\infty} \Phi_{oo}(\omega)\,d\omega},
$$

$$
D = \frac{\displaystyle\iint_{-\infty}^{+\infty} [1 - 2\tau(\omega) + |\tau(\omega)|^2]\Phi_{oo}(\omega)\,d\omega}{\displaystyle\iint_{-\infty}^{+\infty} \Phi_{oo}(\omega)\,d\omega}.
$$

So far so good. The system is described by $\tau(\omega)$, the object structure by $\Phi_{oo}(\omega)$, and the use of the instrument will dictate the choice of quality factor. However, to proceed it is necessary to make some assumptions concerning $\Phi_{oo}(\omega)$. In the absence of specific data, we will make an appeal to information theory and invoke what we may call the principle of maximum ignorance. We shall choose for $\Phi_{oo}(\omega)$ the form of "white" (i.e., flat at least up to the cutoff of the filter) Gaussian noise. The Gaussian requirement comes about from the condition that of all object structures having a fixed mean square value, the one whose sampled values are Gaussianly distributed has maximum entropy. Choosing a spectrum that is flat up to the resolution limit allows us to pull $\Phi_{oo}(\omega)$ outside the integral and concentrate on the way these assessment factors depend on the system through $\tau(\omega)$.

With these simplifying assumptions, we proceed to define new quality factors normalized to those of an ideal instrument through the relations

$$
t = \frac{T}{T_0} = \frac{\displaystyle\iint_{-\infty}^{+\infty} |\tau(\omega)|^2\,d\omega}{\displaystyle\iint_{-\infty}^{+\infty} |\tau_0(\omega)|^2\,d\omega}, \qquad
q = \frac{Q}{Q_0} = \frac{\displaystyle\iint_{-\infty}^{+\infty} \tau(\omega)\,d\omega}{\displaystyle\iint_{-\infty}^{+\infty} \tau_0(\omega)\,d\omega},
$$

$$
f = \frac{F}{F_0} = \frac{q - \eta t}{1 - \eta},
$$

where

$$
\eta = \frac{T_0}{2Q_0} = \text{const.}
$$

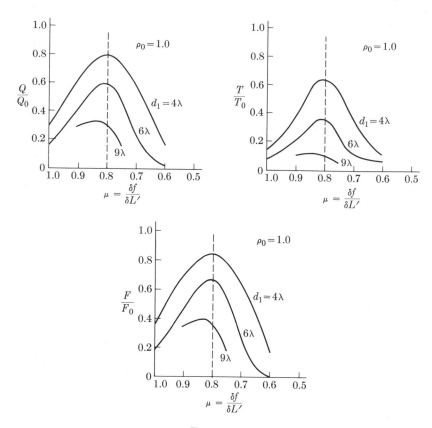

<figure>FIGURE 7–1</figure>

We point out again, for emphasis, that T being insensitive to the phase of $\tau(\omega)$ does not penalize the system for producing "spurious resolution." Furthermore, q as defined here, is identical to the Strehl definition $\mathfrak{D}$. And finally, T is just the term that Schade [2] originally used to rate systems, and he labeled N_e, the equivalent pass band.

We close this section with an illustration of the way these quality factors vary with focal setting for several ratios of third- to fifth-order spherical aberration. From Fig. 6–1, Chapter 6, we see that one can just about reach the Maréchal tolerance by fully correcting ($\rho_0 = 1$) and focusing at $\mu = 0.8$ for 4λ of fifth-order spherical aberration. As d_1 exceeds 4λ, we see from Fig. 7–1 that there is a definite tendency for all three curves to shift towards the zonal focus*. In Fig. 7–2, we see that for the over-corrected case ($\rho_0 = 0.9$), once again there is a shift from the best focus

---

* That is, on a normalized basis. $\delta L'$ itself increases with d_1.

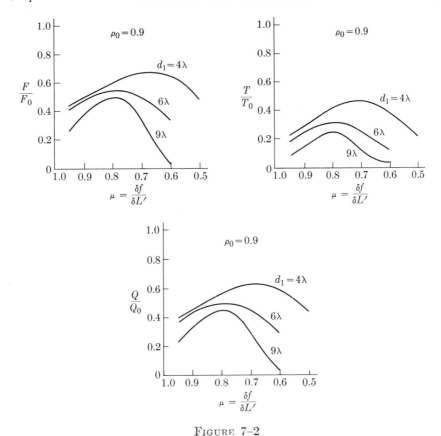

FIGURE 7–2

for small aberrations ($\mu \cong 0.65$) towards the zonal focus. These shifts are in line with what we would expect from purely geometrical considerations for large aberrations.

7–2 Further statistical considerations: graininess and granularity

So far we have been concerned with the problem of forming the optical image without regard to the question of noise either due to the photon fluctuations themselves or due to the receptor (eye, photocell, film, etc.). In photographic applications the fluctuations due to the irregular grain structure are the principal source of noise. Of course from an information-theoretic point of view both the band-width (resolution) and noise (granularity) limitations must be included in order to render a finite informational density in bits per mm². This is true of all measurements in physics. Every real physical signal is limited in time, space and frequency. Further,

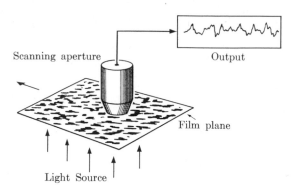

FIGURE 7-3

all measurements are accompanied by noise. The band-width restriction determines the finite number of degrees of freedom of the waveform, but without noise one could indefinitely distinguish one sampled ordinate from its neighbor.

In an attempt to shed a little light on this question of granularity and, at the same time, to carry out an instructive example of calculating correlation functions and statistical spectra in two dimensions, we now wish to examine two simple models.

Consider first the situation depicted in Fig. 7-3. In this figure, we let $T(\xi, \eta)$ represent the point-by-point transmission, and we denote by A the area of the scanning aperture. We shall be concerned with transmission fluctuation about the mean, defined as

$$t(\xi, \eta) = T(\xi, \eta) - \overline{T},$$

where

$$\overline{T} = \lim_{A \to \infty} \frac{1}{A} \iint\limits_{A} T(\xi, \eta) \, d\xi \, d\eta.$$

We shall also need the autocorrelation function,

$$\phi_{tt}(x, y) = \overline{t(\xi, \eta) t(\xi + x, \eta + y)}$$

$$= \lim_{A \to \infty} \frac{1}{A} \iint\limits_{A} t(\xi, \eta) t(\xi + x, \eta + y) \, d\xi \, d\eta$$

$$= \phi_{TT}(x, y) - (\overline{T})^2; \tag{7-1}$$

at the origin, this function becomes

$$\phi_{tt}(0, 0) = \overline{t^2} = \overline{(T - \overline{T})^2} = \sigma_T^2.$$

The statistical spectrum of these fluctuations is defined by the Wiener-Khinchin theorem as

$$\Phi_{tt}(\omega_x, \omega_y) = \int\!\!\!\int\limits_{-\infty}^{+\infty} \phi_{tt}(x, y)e^{-i\omega \cdot \mathbf{r}} \, dx \, dy.$$

So much for the actual fluctuations on the sample. As we scan we receive a blurred version of those undulations. If $s(\xi, \eta)$ describes the intensity impulse response of the scanning aperture then the *observed* fluctuations will be given by

$$t'(x, y) = \int\!\!\!\int\limits_{-\infty}^{+\infty} s(x - \xi, y - \eta)t(\xi, \eta) \, d\xi \, d\eta.$$

In frequency space, we have

$$\Phi'_{tt}(\omega_x, \omega_y) = |\tau(\omega_x, \omega_y)|^2 \Phi_{tt}(\omega_x, \omega_y),$$

and once more, taking the Fourier transform, we have for the output autocorrelation function,

$$\phi'_{tt}(x, y) = \overline{t'(\xi, \eta)t'(\xi + x, \eta + y)}$$

$$= \frac{1}{4\pi^2} \int\!\!\!\int\limits_{-\infty}^{+\infty} \Phi'_{tt}(\omega_x, \omega_y)e^{i\omega \cdot \mathbf{r}} \, d\omega_x \, d\omega_y$$

$$= \frac{1}{4\pi^2} \int\!\!\!\int\limits_{-\infty}^{+\infty} |\tau(\omega_x, \omega_y)|^2 \Phi_{tt}(\omega_x, \omega_y)e^{i\omega \cdot \mathbf{r}} \, d\omega_x \, d\omega_y. \qquad (7\text{–}2)$$

Before proceeding, we should inject an historical note. First we must distinguish between the concepts of graininess and granularity. *Graininess* refers to the subjective impression of the random fluctuations on a sample and is defined [3] operationally in terms of the magnification at which the grains appear to blend. The term *granularity*, on the other hand, has been reserved to describe objective measurements with a physical device on the grain structure. One of the early granularity factors proposed by Goetz and Gould [4] is defined as $G = 1000 \sqrt{2} \, \sigma'_T$ where σ'_T is the measured standard deviation in transmission, as an aperture of area A scans the sample. Later, Selwyn [5], who recognized the visual dependence on density D, suggested the factor $S = \sqrt{2A} \, \sigma'_D$. For apertures much larger than the grain size S vs. $\sqrt{A}$ should be constant. Later, to bring objective methods more into line with graininess rankings, Jones and Higgins [6] urged that the average density difference between two adjacent scanning apertures be adopted as the granularity factor. Combining the syzygetic granularity coefficient $\overline{SAD}$ with a threshold gradient-sensitivity curve of the eye, they succeeded in determining the subjective graininess ranking. Still later [7, 8], the autocorrelation and its Fourier transform, the statistical spectrum, were suggested as the proper measure of granularity. Finally, Marriage and Pitts [9] demonstrated the mathematical equivalence of the various factors.

With this background let us now examine Eq. 7–2 at the origin:

$$\sigma_T'^2 = \overline{(T' - \overline{T'})^2} = \overline{(t')^2} = \phi'_{tt}(0, 0)$$

$$= \frac{1}{4\pi^2} \int\int\limits_{-\infty}^{+\infty} |\tau(\omega)|^2 \Phi_{tt}(\omega) \, d\omega_x \, d\omega_y$$

$$= \int\int\limits_{-\infty}^{+\infty} \phi_{tt}(x, y) \phi_{ss}(x, y) \, dx \, dy, \qquad (7\text{–}3)$$

where the last step follows from Parseval's theorem and where $\phi_{ss}(x, y)$ is the self-convolution of the impulse response. As the volume under the product $\phi_{tt}\phi_{ss}$, the last equation has an interesting interpretation. Let us examine its two extremes. First, if the scanning aperture is much smaller than the grain size then $\phi_{ss}(x, y)$ approaches $\delta(x, y)$. Making this substitution and using the sifting property of the delta function, we get

$$\sigma_T'^2 = \phi_{tt}(0, 0) = \sigma_T^2.$$

If, on the other hand, the scanning aperture is much larger than the grain size, then $\phi_{ss}(x, y)$ is approximately constant $[\phi_{ss}(0, 0)]$ over the correlation range of the grains and can be pulled outside the integral:

$$\sigma_T'^2 = \phi_{ss}(0, 0) \int\int\limits_{-\infty}^{+\infty} \phi_{tt}(x, y) \, dx \, dy. \qquad (7\text{–}4)$$

For a given film type, the integral is a constant. To determine the dependence of $\phi_{ss}(0, 0)$ on the scanning-aperture size, we write the transfer function in dimensionless units $\tau(\mu, \nu)$ so that if the scanning aperture changes its size but not its shape, $\tau(\mu, \nu)$ does not change. The dimensionless units are defined as

$$\mu = \frac{\omega_x}{(\omega_x)_{\max}}, \qquad \nu = \frac{\omega_y}{(\omega_y)_{\max}},$$

where

$$(\omega_x)_{\max} \cong \frac{2\pi}{x_{\max}}, \qquad (\omega_y)_{\max} \cong \frac{2\pi}{y_{\max}};$$

x_{max} and y_{max} being the maximum dimensions of the scanning aperture. From the Fourier transform relation between $\phi_{ss}(x, y)$ and $|\tau(\omega_x, \omega_y)|^2$, we can now write

$$\phi_{ss}(0, 0) \sim \frac{1}{A} \int\limits_{-\infty}^{+\infty}\!\!\int |\tau(\mu, \nu)|^2 \, d\mu \, d\nu = \frac{\text{const}}{A}.$$

Substituting this back into Eq. 7–4, we have

$$\sigma'_T \sqrt{A} = \text{const},$$

which has been confirmed from observations [6]. Continuing to assume that we have apertures much larger than the grain size, we can also determine the expression for the density fluctuations. From the definition of photographic density $D = \log_{10} 1/T$, we can write

$$\Delta D = D - \overline{D} = -\log_{10}\left(1 + \frac{T - \overline{T}}{\overline{T}}\right)$$

$$= -0.4343\left[\frac{\Delta T}{\overline{T}} - \frac{1}{2}\left(\frac{\Delta T}{\overline{T}}\right)^2 + \frac{1}{3}\left(\frac{\Delta T}{\overline{T}}\right)^3 - \cdots\right],$$

and for large scanning apertures, $\Delta T/\overline{T} \ll 1$, leading to

$$\sigma_D = \sqrt{\overline{\Delta D^2}} = \frac{0.4343}{\overline{T}} \sigma_T.$$

Hence $S = \sqrt{2A}\, \sigma'_D$ versus $\sqrt{A}$ should also be constant for large scanning apertures.

We now want to determine the way in which the standard deviation in observed transmission varies as the scanning aperture increases. To this end, we now propose to consider two much simplified models of grain.

7–3 Checkerboard model

With reference to the checkerboard pattern of Fig. 7–4, we assume that a section of this pattern is covered by a square aperture of area $A = L^2$ containing a total of N squares, m of which are clear and n of which are black (grains). Further, each grain has an area $a = l^2$ and the probability of choosing, at random, a clear area from a large population is just the ratio of clear to total area and is given by $p = \overline{m}/N = \overline{T}$ where $\overline{T}$ is the macroscopic transmission. Finally the total number of squares in A is

$$N = \frac{A}{a} = \frac{L^2}{l^2} = m + n.$$

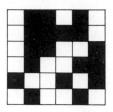

FIGURE 7–4

For an area A containing a total of N squares, the probability* that m of them will be white is given by the binomial distribution

$$P_N(m) = \frac{N!}{m!(N - m)!} p^m (1 - p)^{N-m}; \qquad p = \overline{T}.$$

For a large population, the binomial distribution has first and second moments given by

$$\overline{m} = pN = \overline{T}N, \qquad \sigma_m^2 = pqN = \overline{T}(1 - \overline{T})N.$$

We can use this latter expression to verify the Selwyn root-area law. Since

$$\sigma_T^2 = \overline{(T - \overline{T})^2} = \overline{\left(\frac{m}{N}\right)^2} - \left(\frac{\overline{m}}{N}\right)^2 = \frac{\sigma_m^2}{N^2},$$

we have

$$\sigma_T^2 = \frac{\overline{T}(1 - \overline{T})}{N} = \frac{a\overline{T}(1 - \overline{T})}{A},$$

indicating that $\sigma_T \sqrt{A}$ is constant. For a smaller population, we must exercise some care. It is not difficult to show that the correlation function for this model has the form

$$\phi_{tt}(x, y) = \overline{T}(1 - \overline{T})\left(1 - \frac{|x|}{l}\right)\left(1 - \frac{|y|}{l}\right), \qquad |x| \leq l, \qquad |y| \leq l,$$
$$= 0, \qquad\qquad\qquad\qquad\qquad |x| > l, \qquad |y| > l,$$

with a spectrum of the form

$$\Phi_{tt}(\omega_x, \omega_y) = \overline{T}(1 - \overline{T})l^2 \operatorname{sinc}^2 \frac{\omega_x l}{2} \operatorname{sinc}^2 \frac{\omega_y l}{2}.$$

For the scanning aperture, it is equally easy to demonstrate that

$$\phi_{ss}(x, y) = L^2\left(1 - \frac{|x|}{L}\right)\left(1 - \frac{|y|}{L}\right), \qquad |x| \leq L, \qquad |y| \leq L,$$
$$= 0, \qquad\qquad\qquad\qquad\qquad |x| > L, \qquad |y| > L.$$

---

* See Appendix B.

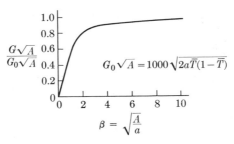

FIGURE 7–5

By substituting $\phi_{ss}(x, y)$ and $\phi_{tt}(x, y)$ into Eq. (7–3) and performing the integration, we get

$$\sigma'_T = \sqrt{\overline{T}(1 - \overline{T})} \left(1 - \frac{\beta}{3}\right), \qquad \beta < 1,$$

$$= \sqrt{\overline{T}(1 - \overline{T})} \, \frac{3\beta - 1}{3\beta^2}, \qquad \beta \geq 1,$$

where

$$\beta = \frac{L}{l} = \sqrt{A/a}.$$

Figure 7–5 shows how $G\sqrt{A}$ varies with $\sqrt{A}$ and the interested reader should compare this result with similar curves [6] describing measurements made on real grain structures. Before closing this section, we point out that the extension to σ'_D is by no means straightforward. For small scanning apertures, the concept of photographic density begins to lose its meaning. The logarithmic dependence on T for small scanning apertures causes D to pass through large excursions. As a result one ends up more with a description of the saturation properties of the microdensitometer than with the actual fluctuations existing on the sample if the size of the scanning aperture is allowed to approach a few grain diameters.

7–4 Overlapping circular grain model

We turn now to a slightly more realistic model [3] of grain structures; namely that shown in Fig. 7–6. This treatment of the transmission and autocorrelation function was first given by Picinbono [10]. It involves more than a mere two-dimensional extension of the random two-level waveform with Poisson distributed crossings that is so well known in electrical communication theory. To begin with, we assume that (a) the grains are circular and the centers of these circles fall at random on a plate as independent events; (b) the grain centers are Poisson distributed;

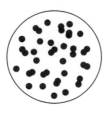

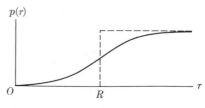

FIGURE 7-6   FIGURE 7-7

i.e., the probability that there are n grains in an area A is given by

$$P_n(A) = \frac{\bar{n}^n e^{-\bar{n}}}{n!},$$

where $d = \bar{n}/A$ is the population density; (c) the grain sizes follow the distribution law

$$p(r) = \text{Prob}\,(R < r).$$

In our simplified version we shall take the grains as constant in size; hence $p(r)$ is the dotted curve (Fig. 7-7).

As before $T(x, y)$ is the point by point transmission assuming the values either 0 or 1. We now wish to calculate the gross transmission or expectation value of the transmission

$$\mathcal{E}(T) = \bar{T} = \lim_{A \to \infty} \frac{1}{A} \iint_A T(x, y)\, dx\, dy. \tag{7-5}$$

We now divide the plane into cells a_i. We attach to a_i the following properties: $[B]$ if it does not contain a center (x_i, y_i) of a grain extending, to (x, y), and $[\bar{B}]$ if it does contain a center (x_i, y_i) of a grain extending to (x, y). Next, we define p_i as the probability that cell a_i has the property B. From Eq. (7-5), we can break up the region of integration into two parts: that for which $T = 1$ and that for which $T = 0$. Then $\bar{T}$ is just the ratio of clear to total area. Equivalently, $\bar{T}$ is the fraction of the total number of times that a point sampling aperture placed at random records $T = 1$. In other words, $\bar{T} = \text{Prob}\,[T = 1]$. But this can come about only if the cells a_i surrounding (x, y) have the property B. Therefore

$$\bar{T} = \prod_i p_i, \tag{7-6}$$

where we now choose, for convenience, the geometry of the cells a_i to be annular rings of area $2\pi r_i\, dr_i$ centered on (x, y). (See Fig. 7-8.) Let us now enumerate the number of ways that cell a_i can have the property B. First it may contain no grain centers, or it may contain one which does not

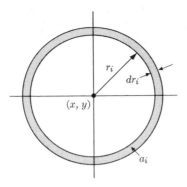

FIGURE 7–8

reach (x, y), or it may contain two grain centers, neither of which reach (x, y), etc., etc. In terms of the Poisson and size distributions, we have

$$p_i = P_0(a_i) + P_1(a_i)p(r_i) + P_2(a_i)p^2(r_i) + \cdots + P_n(a_i)p^n(r_i)$$

$$= e^{-\overline{n}_i} + \frac{\overline{n}_i}{1!}e^{-\overline{n}_i}p(r_i) + \cdots + \frac{\overline{n}_i^n e^{-\overline{n}_i}}{n!}\, p^n(r_i)$$

$$= e^{-\overline{n}_i[1-p(r_i)]},$$

where $\overline{n}_i = a_i d = 2d\pi r_i\, dr_i$. Substituting back into Eq. (7–6), we get

$$\overline{T} = \prod_i p_i = e^{-\sum_i \overline{n}_i[1-p(r_i)]}$$

and passing from the summation to the integral, we have

$$\overline{T} = \exp\left\{-2\pi d \int_0^\infty [1 - p(r)]r\, dr\right\}.$$

For the case in which all grains are of the same size, this reduces to

$$\overline{T} = e^{-\pi R^2 d} = e^{-(\overline{n}a)/A}, \tag{7–7}$$

where $a = \pi R^2$ is the area of a single grain. This expression makes sense in that, as we start sprinkling grains at random over a clear area, the transmission at first decreases almost linearly with population density, but as overlapping sets in, the transmission decreases exponentially with population density. In fact, associating the photographic density D with the population density through the relation $D = Ma(\overline{n}/A)$, where $M = \log_{10} e = 0.4343$, Eq. (7–7) can be inverted to yield

$$D = \log_{10} \frac{1}{\overline{T}},$$

which is the more common way of describing the exponential decay of $\overline{T}$ with d. Finally, before turning to the calculation of the autocorrelation function for this model, we point out that, because T is restricted to the values 0 or 1, $T^2 = T$ at every point. Hence

$$\sigma_T^2 = \overline{(T - \overline{T})^2} = \overline{T^2} - (\overline{T})^2$$
$$= \overline{T}(1 - \overline{T}).$$

So far as the correlation function is concerned, we can expect it to display rotational symmetry, depending only upon the distance between two points. For this reason we shall simplify matters by taking the two points along the x-axis a distance l apart. From the definition of the correlation function

$$\phi_{TT}(l) = \lim_{A \to \infty} \frac{1}{A} \iint_A T(x, y) T(x - l, y) \, dx \, dy.$$

In performing the averaging, four possibilities arise for $T(x, y)$ and $T(x - l, y)$. All will be zero except when $T(x, y)$ *and* $T(x - l, y)$ are both equal to one. In short,

$$\phi_{TT}(l) = \text{Prob} \left[T(x, y) T(x - l, y) = 1 \right].$$

We now redefine a_i such that it possesses the property $[B]$ if it does not contain the center of a grain (x_i, y_i) extending to (x, y) nor to $(x - l, y)$; $[\overline{B}]$ otherwise. Further, we divide the plane into half planes as shown in Fig. 7–9.

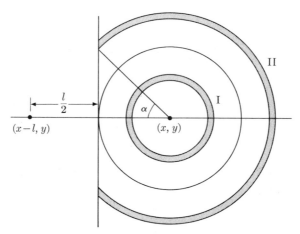

FIGURE 7–9

We now define the following symbols:

P_{I} = probability that the annular rings in region I $(r < l/2)$ have property B.

P_{II} = probability that the truncated annular rings in region II $(r \geq l/2)$ have property B.

Hence $P_{\mathrm{I}} \times P_{\mathrm{II}}$ is the probability that the grains in the right half plane leave (x, y) and $(x - l, y)$ uncovered. Since there is independence between the two half planes, we have

$$\phi_{TT}(l) = \mathrm{Prob}\,[T(x, y)T(x - l, y) = 1] = (P_{\mathrm{I}} \times P_{\mathrm{II}})^2.$$

From previous considerations, we can write, immediately,

$$P_{\mathrm{I}} = \exp\left\{-2\pi d \int_0^{l/2} [1 - p(r)]r\,dr\right\},$$

and

$$P_{\mathrm{II}} = \exp\left\{-2\pi d \int_{l/2}^{\infty} \int_{\cos^{-1}l/2r}^{\pi} [1 - p(r)]r\,dr\,d\alpha\right\},$$

so that

$$\phi_{TT}(l) = \exp\left\{-4d\left\{\pi \int_0^{\infty} [1 - p(r)]r\,dr - \int_{l/2}^{\infty} \cos^{-1}\frac{l}{2r}[1 - p(r)]r\,dr\right\}\right\}.$$

We must now distinguish two regions. For $l/2 > R$, the second integral in the exponent vanishes, leaving

$$\phi_{TT}(l) = e^{-2\pi R^2 d} = (\overline{T})^2; \qquad \frac{l}{2} > R,$$

as we should expect. For $l/2 \leq R$ both integrals contribute to yield

$$\phi_{TT}(l) = (\overline{T})^2 e^{\pi R^2 F(l/2R)d}; \qquad \frac{l}{2} \leq R,$$

where

$$F\left(\frac{l}{2R}\right) = \frac{2}{\pi}\left[\cos^{-1}\frac{l}{2R} - \frac{l}{2R}\sqrt{1 - \left(\frac{l}{2R}\right)^2}\right]$$

is just the same function that we encountered in diffraction theory describing the self-convolution of two circles. It enters here, of course, for entirely different reasons. (See Fig. 7–10.) It is a little more convenient to transform from $\phi_{TT}(l)$ to $\phi_{tt}(l)$ through Eq. (7–1). We then have

$$\phi_{tt}(l) = (\overline{T})^2[e^{(D/M)F(l/2R)} - 1], \qquad 0 \leq l \leq 2R,$$

$$= 0, \qquad\qquad\qquad l > 2R,$$

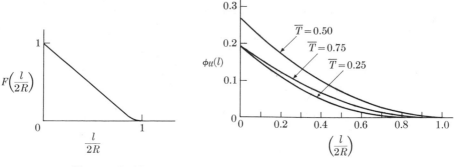

FIGURE 7–10   FIGURE 7–11

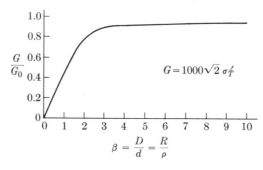

FIGURE 7–12

where $M = \log_{10} e = 0.4343$ and D is the photographic density. Curves of this function are shown in Fig. 7–11. It is an easy matter to consider what happens as this model is scanned by a circular aperture of radius ρ. The transfer function is $\tau(\omega) = 2J_1(\omega\rho)/\omega\rho$ and for $\phi_{ss}(l)$ we have

$$\phi_{ss}(l) = \pi\rho^2 F\left(\frac{l}{2\rho}\right), \qquad 0 \leq l \leq 2\rho,$$
$$= 0, \qquad l > 2\rho.$$

Substituting these expressions into Eq. 7–3 and performing the integration, we get the curve shown in Fig. 7–12. Once again the reader is invited to compare this with curves obtained with real grain structures appearing in the literature [6]. Lastly, Picinbono [10] and his followers [11] have extended this treatment to include frequency distribution of both grain sizes and grain transmittances.

REFERENCES

1. E. H. LINFOOT, *J. Opt. Soc. Am.* **46,** 740 (1956).
2. O. H. SCHADE, *J. S. M. P. T. E.* **58** (1952).
3. J. H. WEBB, *J. Opt. Soc. Am.* **45,** 379 (1955).
4. A. GOETZ and W. O. GOULD, *J. S. M. P.* **29,** 510 (1937).
5. E. W. H. SELWYN, *Phot. J.* **79,** 513 (1939).
6. L. A. JONES and G. C. HIGGINS, *J. Opt. Soc. Am.* **35,** 435 (1945); **36,** 203 (1946); **37,** 217 (1947); **38,** 393 (1948); **41,** 41 (1951); **41,** 64 (1951); **41,** 192 (1951).
7. P. FELLGETT, *J. Opt. Soc. Am.* **43,** 271 (1953).
8. R. C. JONES, *J. Opt. Soc. Am.* **45,** 799 (1955).
9. A. MARRIAGE and E. PITTS, *J. Opt. Soc. Am.* **46,** 1019 (1956); **47** (1957).
10. B. PICINBONO, *Comptes Rendus,* **240,** 2206 (1955).
11. M. SAVELLI, *Comptes Rendus,* **246,** 3605 (1958).

8

Matrix and Coherence Theory

8-1 Introduction: Wolf's mutual coherence function

For the most part, we have confined our attention to the analysis and synthesis of optical systems in which the illumination is incoherent. Only when looking for special effects did we make an abrupt change to a system for which the complex amplitude added linearly from point to point. Surely we must expect a continuous transition between these extreme limits. Such a transitional region exists and is known as the field of partial coherence. An exceptionally valuable historical account together with a thorough exposition of the subject appears in the excellent book by Born and Wolf [1]. We shall adopt here a phenomenological approach, insofar as the theory of partial coherence relates to problems of image formation.

There is no surprise that the disturbances at two points in space and time should be correlated, either from a classical or a quantum point of view. A beam of light emanating from a source of area σ and spectral width $\Delta\nu$ should produce coherence effects [2] in a region $c/\Delta\nu$ along the beam, and for two points across the beam that fall within the diffraction disk if σ were treated as a diffracting aperture. This coherence volume in real space, corresponding to a cell in phase space, should show photon degeneracy. It is well known that the symmetry properties of the wave function for bosons leads directly to an "attraction" or clumping. Much of the interest in coherence theory stems, in fact, from the much discussed Hanbury Brown-Twiss experiment [3], and the development of lasers for which, as Mandel [2] has pointed out, the degeneracy can range from 10^{-3} in the former to 10^{12} for the gas laser.

Recognizing the need for casting optics into the language of observables, Wolf [4] has shown that the mutual coherence function $\Gamma(\mathbf{x}_1, \mathbf{x}_2; \tau)$ is a useful and meaningful way to describe the correlation between the optical disturbances at two points in space-time. Starting with the real optical disturbance, e.g., one of the cartesian components of the electric vector, we decompose it into its Fourier representation over positive frequencies,

$$V^r(t) = \int_0^\infty a(\nu) \cos[\phi(\nu) - 2\pi\nu t]\, d\nu.$$

Associated with this real disturbance is the complex disturbance known as the analytic signal defined by

$$V(t) = V^{(r)}(t) + iV^{(i)}(t),$$

where

$$V^{(i)}(t) = \int_0^\infty a(v) \sin [\phi(v) - 2\pi vt] \, dv;$$

$V^{(r)}(t)$ and $V^{(i)}(t)$ are not unrelated, however. The fact that the Fourier spectrum of $V(t)$ vanishes for negative frequencies implies that $V^{(r)}(t)$ and $V^{(i)}(t)$ are Hilbert transform pairs,

$$V^{(i)}(t) = \frac{1}{\pi} P \int_{-\infty}^\infty \frac{V^{(r)}(t')}{t' - t} \, dt', \qquad V^{(r)}(t) = -\frac{1}{\pi} P \int_{-\infty}^\infty \frac{V^{(i)}(t')}{t' - t} \, dt',$$

where P denotes the principal value at $t' = t$. However, $V^{(r)}(t)$ and hence $V(t)$ are not observables at optical frequencies. Their mean square content taken over long time averages are observable and are related through the equation,

$$\langle V^{(r)^2}(t) \rangle = \langle V^{(i)^2}(t) \rangle = \tfrac{1}{2} \langle |V(t)|^2 \rangle = 2 \int_0^\infty G(v) \, dv,$$

where

$$G(v) = \lim_{T \to \infty} \frac{|v_T(v)|^2}{2T}$$

is the power spectrum of $V^{(r)}(t)$ treated as a stationary stochastic function, and where the brackets $\langle \ \rangle$ indicate a time average. With this brief introduction, we now proceed to define Wolf's mutual coherence function in terms of the cross correlation of the complex disturbance at two points in space at different times,

$$\Gamma(\mathbf{x}_1, \mathbf{x}_2; \tau) = \Gamma_{12}(\tau) = \langle V(\mathbf{x}_1, t + \tau) V^*(\mathbf{x}_2, t) \rangle.$$

We mention in passing that $\Gamma_{12}(0)$ represents the correlation at two points in space at the same time, and, being proportional to the contrast of the fringes in the Michelson stellar interferometer, its spatial Fourier transform yields information concerning the brightness across the source. Similarly $\Gamma_{11}(\tau)$ represents the correlation at one point in space at two instants in time and, being proportional to the contrast of the fringes in the Michelson two-beam interferometer, its time-Fourier transform yields information concerning the spectral energy distribution of the source. In short, the Michelson stellar interferometer is a spatial harmonic analyzer, and the two-beam interferometer is a temporal† harmonic [5] analyzer.

---

† In practice, of course, it is the optical path $\Delta = c\tau$ which is varied.

Closely associated with the mutual coherence function is the normalized complex degree of coherence which is defined as

$$\gamma_{12}(\tau) = \frac{\Gamma_{12}(\tau)}{\sqrt{I_1}\sqrt{I_2}},$$

where $I_1 = \Gamma_{11}(0)$ and $I_2 = \Gamma_{22}(0)$ are the intensities at points P_1 and P_2, respectively. The amplitude and phase of $\gamma_{12}(\tau)$ can be operationally defined in terms of the contrast and position of the fringes produced by allowing the light to interfere from pinholes at P_1 and P_2 in an otherwise opaque screen.

8–2 Image formation

Because of the linearity of the Maxwell equations and the fact that $V^r(t)$ satisfies the scalar wave equation, it can be shown [6] that $\Gamma_{12}(\tau)$ satisfies a pair of wave equations in the form

$$\nabla_s^2 \Gamma(\mathbf{x}_1, \mathbf{x}_2; \tau) = \frac{1}{c^2}\frac{\partial^2 \Gamma(\mathbf{x}_1, \mathbf{x}_2, \tau)}{\partial \tau^2}, \qquad s = 1, 2.$$

This is very important from the standpoint of image formation. The entire notion of treating optical systems in the coherent or incoherent limits as filters of spatial frequencies is based on the linear transformation of Fourier components between object and image planes. In partially coherent light, the Fourier components of the object structure become "scrambled" [7] and enter into the formation of the image in a nonlinear way. Although it is true that these components can always be "unscrambled" if care is taken, it is more desirable to preserve the linear formulation in terms of $\Gamma(\mathbf{x}_1, \mathbf{x}_2; \tau)$ between the object and image planes and later pass to the limits.

With this objective in mind, we now symbolize an optical system in terms of the three planes shown in Fig. 8–1. In this figure, the vector $\boldsymbol{\xi}$ refers to a point in the object plane, $\boldsymbol{\beta}$ refers to a point in the pupil plane and $\mathbf{x}$ is a point in the image plane. If we decompose $\Gamma_{12}(\tau)$ in the form

$$\Gamma_{12}(\tau) = \int_{-\infty}^{\infty} \hat{\Gamma}_{12}(\nu)e^{-2\pi i\nu\tau}\,d\nu$$

and substitute into the wave equations, we find that $\hat{\Gamma}_{12}(\nu)$ satisfies a pair of Helmholtz equations; and, from Chapter 5, we already know something about the solutions of these equations, for problems like this. Solving the first of these equations, we have,

$$\hat{\Gamma}(\mathbf{x}_1, \boldsymbol{\xi}_2; \nu) = \int u(\mathbf{x}_1, \boldsymbol{\xi}_1; \nu)\hat{\Gamma}(\boldsymbol{\xi}_1, \boldsymbol{\xi}_2; \nu)\,d\boldsymbol{\xi}_1 \qquad (8\text{–}1)$$

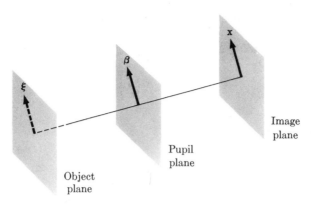

Image
plane

Pupil
plane

Object
plane

FIGURE 8-1

where $u(\mathbf{x}_1 \boldsymbol{\xi}_1; \nu)$ is the complex disturbance at $\mathbf{x}_1$ due to a point source at $\boldsymbol{\xi}_1$, at a frequency ν. For the second of the Helmholtz equations, we have

$$\hat{\Gamma}(\mathbf{x}_1, \mathbf{x}_2; \nu) = \int u^*(\mathbf{x}_2, \boldsymbol{\xi}_2; \nu)\hat{\Gamma}(\mathbf{x}_1, \boldsymbol{\xi}_2; \nu)\, d\boldsymbol{\xi}_2 \tag{8-2}$$

where the complex conjugate of $u(\mathbf{x}_2, \boldsymbol{\xi}_2; \nu)$ has been chosen to insure that

$$\hat{\Gamma}(\mathbf{x}_1, \mathbf{x}_2; \nu) = \hat{\Gamma}^*(\mathbf{x}_2, \mathbf{x}_1; \nu)$$

a condition imposed from the definition of $\Gamma(\mathbf{x}_1, \mathbf{x}_2; \tau)$ and the assumption of stationarity that

$$\Gamma(\mathbf{x}_1, \mathbf{x}_2; \tau) = \Gamma(\mathbf{x}_2 - \mathbf{x}_1; \tau).$$

Substituting Eq. (8-1) into Eq. (8-2), we arrive at the relation which describes the way in which each spectral component of the mutual coherence function propagates between the object and image planes;

$$\hat{\Gamma}(\mathbf{x}_1, \mathbf{x}_2; \nu) = \iint u(\mathbf{x}_1, \boldsymbol{\xi}_1; \nu)u^*(\mathbf{x}_2, \boldsymbol{\xi}_2; \nu)\hat{\Gamma}(\boldsymbol{\xi}_1, \boldsymbol{\xi}_2; \nu)\, d\boldsymbol{\xi}_1\, d\boldsymbol{\xi}_2.$$

Taking the time-Fourier transform and imposing the spatially stationary condition on the complex point image distribution, we have, finally,

$$\Gamma(\mathbf{x}_1, \mathbf{x}_2; \tau)$$
$$= \iiint u(\boldsymbol{\xi}_1 - \mathbf{x}_1; \nu)u^*(\boldsymbol{\xi}_2 - \mathbf{x}_2; \nu)\hat{\Gamma}(\boldsymbol{\xi}_1, \boldsymbol{\xi}_2; \nu)e^{-2\pi i\nu\tau}\, d\nu\, d\boldsymbol{\xi}_1\, d\boldsymbol{\xi}_2. \tag{8-3}$$

The intensity distribution is given by letting $\mathbf{x}_2 \to \mathbf{x}_1$ and $\tau \to 0$ yielding $I'(x) = \Gamma_{11}(0)$. Before passing to these limits, we shall first make the quasimonochromatic approximation. Although no optical source produces strictly monochromatic light, in the sense of infinitely long wave trains, there are real situations in which we can assume that $\Delta\nu \ll \bar{\nu}$, where $\Delta\nu$ is the spectral width of the light and $\bar{\nu}$ the mean frequency, reciprocally related to the coherence time $\tau \cong 1/\Delta\nu$. For quasimonochromatic light, we have

$$\Gamma_{12}(\tau) = e^{-2\pi i\bar{\nu}\tau} \int_{-\infty}^{\infty} \hat{\Gamma}_{12}(\nu)e^{-2\pi i(\nu-\bar{\nu})\tau}\,d\nu,$$

and, since

$$(\nu - \bar{\nu})\tau = \Delta\nu\,\tau \cong \frac{\Delta\nu}{\bar{\nu}} \ll 1,$$

we can write

$$\Gamma_{12}(\tau) \cong e^{-2\pi i\bar{\nu}\tau} \int_{-\infty}^{\infty} \hat{\Gamma}_{12}(\nu)\,d\nu$$

$$\cong \Gamma_{12}(0)e^{-2\pi i\bar{\nu}\tau},$$

implying that

$$\hat{\Gamma}_{12}(\nu) \cong \Gamma_{12}(0)\,\delta(\nu - \bar{\nu}).$$

Making the substitution into the right-hand side of Eq. (8–3) and integrating over $d\nu$, we arrive at

$$\Gamma(\mathbf{x}_1, \mathbf{x}_2; \tau) = \iint u(\xi_1 - \mathbf{x}_1; \bar{\nu})u^*(\xi_2 - \mathbf{x}_2; \bar{\nu})\Gamma(\xi_1, \xi_2; 0)\,d\xi_1\,d\xi_2 e^{-2\pi i\bar{\nu}\tau}.$$

$$(8–4)$$

We now specialize still further; for coherent illumination over the object plane, $\Gamma(\xi_1, \xi_2; 0)$ takes the particularly simple form [6]

$$\Gamma(\xi_1, \xi_2; 0) = A(\xi_1)A^*(\xi_2).$$

Substituting this expression into Eq. (8–4), letting

$$\mathbf{x}_2 \to \mathbf{x}_1 = \mathbf{x}, \qquad \tau \to 0,$$

and omitting the dependence on $\bar{\nu}$, we have, for the intensity distribution in the image plane,

$$I'(\mathbf{x}) = \iint_{-\infty}^{\infty} u(\xi_1 - \mathbf{x})u^*(\xi_2 - \mathbf{x})A(\xi_1)A^*(\xi_2)\,d\xi_1\,d\xi_2,$$

or, in better form,

$$I'(\mathbf{x}) = \left| \int_{-\infty}^{\infty} u(\xi - \mathbf{x})A(\xi)\,d\xi \right|^2 \equiv |A'(\mathbf{x})|^2 \qquad (8–5)$$

which emphasizes that the system is a linear filter in complex amplitude. One first computes the coherent superposition between the two planes and then squares it.

For incoherent illumination across the object plane or for a self-luminous object, $\Gamma(\xi_1, \xi_2; 0)$ takes the form

$$\Gamma(\xi_1, \xi_2; 0) = I(\xi_1)\,\delta(\xi_1 - \xi_2).$$

That is, each point radiates independently of every other point. Once again, making the substitution into Eq. (8–4), taking the limits $x_2 \to x_1 = x$, $\tau \to 0$, ignoring the dependence on $\bar{\nu}$, and making use of the sifting property of the delta function, we end up with

$$I'(x) = \int_{-\infty}^{\infty} |u(\xi - x)|^2 I(\xi)\,d\xi, \qquad (8–6)$$

which clearly illustrates the incoherent superposition. In closing this section, we repeat that as superposition integrals, we can write Eq. (8–5) and Eq. (8–6) in the form

$$A'(x) = \int_{-\infty}^{\infty} u(\xi - x)A(\xi)\,d\xi, \qquad \text{coherent limit,}$$

$$I'(x) = \int_{-\infty}^{\infty} s(\xi - x)I(\xi)\,d\xi, \qquad \text{incoherent limit,}$$

where in the first of these expressions $I'(x) = |A'(x)|^2$ and in the second $s(x) = |u(x)|^2$. From the standpoint of linear filter theory, the transfer function in coherent light is the spatial Fourier transform of $u(x)$ which by virtue of Chapter 5 is just $F(\beta)$ the complex amplitude over the exit pupil. Once again, it is just this fact that allows one to exercise control over the Fourier structure of the image in coherent spatial filtering devices and phase contrast microscopy. Finally, in the incoherent case, the transfer function is the spatial Fourier transform of $s(x)$ which, as shown in Eq. (5–9), is the self-convolution of $F(\beta)$, with its complex conjugate.

8–3 Matrix theory

Given a choice, mathematical physicists attempt to describe fields using linear Hermitian operators; linear for obvious reasons, and Hermitian because such operators yield real eigenvalues as observables. Perhaps the best known example in this regard occurred in the early development of the quantum theory. In wave mechanics, the Schrödinger scheme centered about the solution of the basic eigenvalue problems involving a linear second-order differential operator. In Heisenberg's matrix mechanics, the method revolves around the different, but mathematically equivalent, solution of the eigenvalue equation using matrix operators. It is strange, in a way, that the optical wave equation which has been known for a much longer time than the Schrödinger wave equation, has not, until recently, been cast into matrix language. Now, due mainly to the work of Gabor [8] and Gamo [9], there exists today a complete analogue for the matrix and differential descriptions in both wave mechanics and optics. To begin with,‡ we return to Eq. 8–4, and in order to emphasize the salient feature, we confine our attention to one-dimensional variations only. Once again, letting

$$x_2 \rightarrow x_1 = x, \qquad \tau \rightarrow 0$$

and suppressing the explicit dependence on $\bar{\nu}$, we have for the intensity in the image plane,

$$I'(x) = \int\!\!\int_{-\infty}^{\infty} u(\xi_1 - x)u^*(\xi_2 - x)\Gamma(\xi_1, \xi_2) \, d\xi_1 \, d\xi_2. \qquad (8\text{–}7)$$

We now wish to expand $u(x)$ into an orthogonal set of functions. In looking for the proper set, we appeal to the fact that by the very process of diffraction $u(x)$ is band-limited (spatially) to within the numerical aperture of the instrument. Expanding $u(x)$, then, by the sampling theorem, we have

$$u(x) = \sum_{n=-\infty}^{\infty} u\left(\frac{n}{2W}\right) T_n(x),$$

where

$$T_n(x) = \operatorname{sinc}(2\pi Wx - n\pi) = \frac{\sin(2\pi Wx - n\pi)}{(2\pi Wx - n\pi)},$$

and where

$$W = \frac{\sin\theta}{\lambda},$$

θ being the semiaperture angle. Since the sampling theorem is independent of the starting point for the sampled ordinates, we can write

$$u(\xi - x) = \sum_{n=-\infty}^{\infty} u\left(\xi - \frac{n}{2W}\right) T_n(x) = \sum_{n=-\infty}^{\infty} u_n(\xi) T_n(x). \qquad (8\text{–}7a)$$

Substituting Eq. (8–7a) back into Eq. (8–7), we get

$$I'(x) = \sum_m \sum_n T_m^*(x) B_{mn} T_n(x) = \mathbf{T}^\dagger \mathbf{B} \mathbf{T}, \qquad (8\text{–}8)$$

---

‡ The description given here is adapted for image formation from H. Gamo's more elegant treatment (Ref. 13) of wave propagation and detection in matrix language. Some readers may note the obvious similarity between these methods and density matrix techniques (Ref. 14) in other fields.

where the elements B_{mn} of the "illumination matrix" are given by

$$B_{mn} = \iint u_m^*(\xi_2)\Gamma(\xi_1, \xi_2)u_n(\xi_1)\, d\xi_1\, d\xi_2, \tag{8-9}$$

which is a form easily recognized by students of quantum mechanics. Before proceeding, it is instructive to reduce this formulation to Eqs. (8–5) and (8–6) for the coherent and incoherent limits, respectively.

In the coherent limit,

$$\Gamma(\xi_1, \xi_2) = A(\xi_1)A^*(\xi_2)$$

and B_{mn} reduces to

$$B_{mn} = \int u^* \left(\xi_2 - \frac{m}{2W}\right) A^*(\xi_2)\, d\xi_2 \int u\left(\xi_1 - \frac{n}{2W}\right) A(\xi_1)\, d\xi_1$$

$$= A'^* \left(\frac{m}{2W}\right) A'\left(\frac{n}{2W}\right) = A_m'^* A_n'. \tag{8-10}$$

Substituting Eq. (8–10) back into Eq. (8–8) and invoking the sampling theorem once more

$$I'(x) = \left|\sum_n A'\left(\frac{n}{2W}\right) T_n(x)\right|^2 = |A'(x)|^2.$$

For the incoherent limit,

$$\Gamma(\xi_1, \xi_2) = I(\xi_1)\,\delta(\xi_1 - \xi_2)$$

so that B_{mn} reduces to

$$B_{mn} = \int u_m^*(\xi)I(\xi)u_n(\xi)\, d\xi. \tag{8-11}$$

Putting Eq. (8–11) back into Eq. (8–8), we have

$$I'(x) = \int I(\xi)\left[\sum_m u_m^*(\xi)T_m^*(x) \sum_n u_n(\xi)T_n(x)\right]d\xi$$

$$= \int I(\xi)|u(\xi - x)|^2\, d\xi,$$

which agrees, of course, with Eq. (8–6).

Returning to Eqs. (8–8) and (8–9), we note that $I'(x) \geq 0$ and $B_{mn} = B_{nm}^*$, hence $\mathbf{B}$ is a positive definite Hermitian matrix. Further, integrating both sides of Eq. (8–8) over dx and making use of the orthogonal property of the sampling functions, we see that the total illumination in the image plane is just

$$\int I'(x)\, dx = \frac{1}{2W} \sum_m \sum_n B_{mn}\,\delta_{mn} = \frac{1}{2W}\ \text{Trace}\ (\mathbf{B}) = \text{constant}.$$

Suppose now that we define a unitary transformation, such that

$$\mathbf{T} = \mathbf{QS}, \tag{8-12}$$

$$\mathbf{T}^\dagger = (\mathbf{QS})^\dagger = \mathbf{S}^\dagger\mathbf{Q}^\dagger.$$

Equation (8–8) can now be written as

$$I'(x) = \mathbf{S}^\dagger(\mathbf{Q}^\dagger\mathbf{BQ})\mathbf{S}, \tag{8-13}$$

where we now demand of $\mathbf{Q}$ that it diagonalize $\mathbf{B}$ in the form

$$\mathbf{\Lambda} = \mathbf{Q}^\dagger\mathbf{BQ} = \begin{pmatrix} \lambda_1 & & & & \\ & \lambda_2 & & 0 & \\ & & \lambda_3 & & \\ & 0 & & \ddots & \\ & & & & \lambda_N \end{pmatrix}. \tag{8-14}$$

Under these conditions, we can write Eq. (8–13) as

$$I'(x) = \mathbf{S}^\dagger\mathbf{\Lambda S} = \sum_n \lambda_n S_n^2(x). \tag{8-15}$$

Before interpreting this result, we note that the λ_n's are determined by setting $|\mathbf{B} - \mathbf{\Lambda}| = 0$ from the eigenvalue equation (8–14). Substituting these values back into Eq. (8–14) yields the eigenvectors of the unitary transformation in Eq. (8–12) from which $\mathbf{S}$ can be determined.

It is interesting to note that the left-hand side of Eqs. (8–8) and (8–15) are the same. The intensity pattern that we would see or photograph is $I'(x)$. On the other hand, the right-hand sides of these equations lend themselves to an interesting interpretation. As a generalized quadratic form, Eq. (8–8) describes the formation of the image $I'(x)$ of a partially coherent object structure $\Gamma(\xi_1, \xi_2)$ with a lens L_1 whose complex point image is $u(x)$. Equation (8–15), however, states that we would obtain precisely the same observable intensity pattern by first replacing the lens with a second lens whose intensity point image is $S^2(x)$ and then replacing the partially

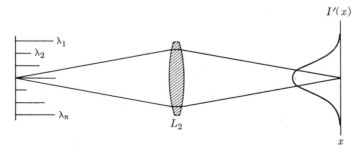

FIGURE 8–2

coherent object structure with a set of equally spaced incoherently radiating points whose brightnesses are $\lambda_1, \lambda_2, \ldots \lambda_n$, as shown in Fig. 8–2.

Since the invariance of the trace of a matrix, under a unitary transformation, corresponds here to the physical fact that the total illumination in the image plane is the same in both representations, we choose, for convenience, to set $\mathrm{Tr}\,\boldsymbol{\Lambda} = \sum_i \lambda_{ii} = 1$. Further, from our interpretation of Eq. (8–15) as an incoherent superposition of beams emanating from sources whose brightnesses are $\lambda_1, \lambda_2, \ldots \lambda_n$, we see that if we had a device which counted individual photons,[*] the probability P_i that a detected photon was associated with the ith beam is just λ_i. From this point of view, it is tempting to construct the entropy (Appendix B) of these light beams in the form

$$H = -\sum_{i=1}^{N} \lambda_i \log \lambda_i.$$

We can now ask under what conditions will H assume a maximum and a minimum, subject to the constraint that $\sum_{i=1}^{N} \lambda_i = 1$? It is an elementary exercise to show that

$$H_{\min} = 0 \quad \text{when} \quad \lambda_j = 1, \qquad \lambda_i = 0, \quad i \neq j,$$

and

$$H_{\max} - \log N \quad \text{when} \quad \lambda_i = \frac{1}{N}, \qquad \text{for all } i.$$

In terms of Fig. 8–2, $H_{\min} = 0$ corresponds to a single bright source in object space indicating no uncertainty as to the source of the detected photons. Maximum H corresponds to the case where all N points are equally bright, indicating maximum uncertainty (entropy). In Appendix B, we show that the eigenvalues λ_i resulting from going to the coherent and incoherent limits in Eqs. (8–10) and (8–11) are just those that lead to H minimum and H maximum, respectively. It is conceptually satisfying that the entropic description of coherent and incoherent light so coincides with our intuitive notions of ordered and disordered superpositions. This idea is by no means new, however, von Laue [10] having been the first to investigate, on thermodynamic grounds, the partially coherent superposition of light beams using entropy. Nor is the result surprising. The value of H is determined by the λ_i's which, as eigenvalues of the illumination matrix, depend upon Wolf's mutual coherence function. A function which already has proven so valuable in describing the properties of partially coherent optical fields.

---

[*] We remind the reader here that the λ's refer to randomness back at the source. We deliberately refrain from associating the concept of a "particle in flight" with the quantum nature of the emission and reception process.

REFERENCES

1. M. Born and E. Wolf, *Principles of Optics*. Pergamon Press (1959).
2. L. Mandel, *J. Opt. Soc. Am.* **51**, 797 (1961).
3. R. Hanbury Brown and R. Q. Twiss, *Nature* **177**, 27 (1956).
4. E. Wolf, *Proc. Roy. Soc. London* **A230**, 246 (1955).
5. A. A. Michelson, *Light Waves and Their Uses*. Univ. of Chicago Press (1902); Phoenix Science Series (1961).
6. G. B. Parrent, *J. Opt. Soc. Am.* **49**, 787 (1959).
7. H. H. Hopkins, *Proc. Roy. Soc. London* **A217**, 408 (1953).
8. W. H. Steel, *Optica Acta* **3**, 49 (1956).
9. D. Gabor, *Astronomical Optics*, Z. Kopal, editor. North-Holland (1956).
10. H. Gamo, *J. Appl. Phys. Japan* **25**, 431 (1956).
11. M. von Laue, *Ann. Phys.* **23** (1907).
12. G. B. Parrent and M. Beran, *Coherence Theory*. Prentice-Hall (in press).
13. H. Gamo, *Progress in Optics*, vol. 3, E. Wolf, editor. North-Holland (in press).
14. D. ter Haar, *Reports on Progress in Physics* **XXIV**, **304** (1961).

9

The Theory of Partial Polarization

9–1 Introduction

So far we have been concerned with the *scalar* theory of light. In the study of partial coherence, for example, we associated a scalar disturbance $V(t)$ at a typical point $\mathbf{x}$ in the field at time t. The theory of partial coherence was then developed in terms of correlation functions. In particular the cross-correlation function of the disturbances at two different points in the field, at two different times, defined as the mutual coherence function $\Gamma_{12}(\tau)$ was found to be very useful. Here, we propose to study the subject of polarization, and subsequently generalize it to the investigation of partial polarization. In doing so, it will be necessary to take into account the *vector* nature of light. As we shall see, the structure of the theory of partial polarization, will have a great deal in common with the theory of partial coherence.

The laws of elementary optics associated with the names of Brewster, and Malus, and the methods of combining two harmonic disturbances at right angles to each other are all too well known to need a description here. These basic concepts are, of course, important and very useful in understanding the underlying physical ideas in the study of polarization. In what follows, we shall concern ourselves mainly with the mathematical formalism that generalizes these basic concepts with a further extension of the possibility of bringing into the formalism the concept of partial polarization. The formalism, apart from being elegant, will be found to introduce considerable simplicity as when the effect of several "polarizing" instruments is to be studied.

Before discussing the formalism, it will be convenient to outline the central idea employed in the modern methods. We restrict ourselves to plane wave fields (monochromatic or otherwise). We assume a plane wave is propagating along the positive z-direction of a suitably chosen space-set of axes, as in Fig. 9–1. A series of optical (polarizing) instruments in cascade (shown as a black box, Fig. 9–1) are then to be thought of as "operating" on the incoming plane wave to produce, subsequently, an outgoing plane wave. In doing so, we must first obtain a suitable "representation" of the plane wave that can be *uniquely* associated with it. The black box is then specified by means of a mathematical "operator." We require that this operator shall be linear. This is in accordance with the

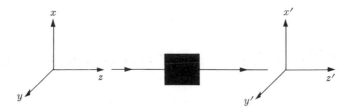

FIGURE 9-1

fact that Maxwell's equations which govern the field (and the mutual coherence function Γ_{12}) that is propagated in accordance with Huygens' principle are all linear. The modern methods to be described in what follows capitalize on the linearity of the problem and take account of the vector nature of light by appealing to matrix methods.

Historically, Stokes [1] (1852) was the first to specify the field in terms of observables, called the four Stokes parameters, one of which refers to the total intensity at a typical point of the field, and the remaining three, as we shall see, specify the state of polarization. Later Poincaré [2] (1892) introduced what is now known as the Poincaré sphere, which we shall study in Section 9-4 after introducing the Stokes parameters. The points on the Poincaré sphere are representative of states of polarization, and the operation of an instrument on the incoming field is then described as the displacement of a typical representative point to a new position on the sphere. Such a geometrical interpretation is indeed satisfying, more so because it gives further insight into the basic physical problem. These ideas were used extensively and applied in the study of both uniaxial and biaxial crystals especially by Pancharatnam [3].

Jones [4] (1941) reconsidered the problem of monochromatic (hence fully polarized) beams and for the first time introduced matrix methods. Jones and his collaborators successfully dealt with the fully polarized wave fields by developing the theory in terms of the field components, and specifying the instrument by a 2 × 2 complex matrix. However, the field components themselves are not the observables of the radiation field at high (optical) frequencies. Realizing this, Mueller [5] made use of the Stokes parameters which are, as we shall see, the observables of the radiation field. The parameters of the outgoing field are then obtained as follows: the instrument is represented by a 4 × 4 (real) matrix (called the Mueller matrix) which operates on the four Stokes parameters displayed as a four-element column vector (the Stokes vector) to yield the Stokes vector of the outgoing field.

The more recent treatments of (partial coherence) partial polarization employ the concepts of correlation functions and "coherency matrices" which were first originated by Wiener [6] and later by Wolf [7]. Further

Wolf [8] stressed the importance of uniquely associating a convenient (complex) representation with the real field, and pointed out the suitability of the analytic signal representation in this respect. Later Parrent and Roman [9] discussed the formal similarity of the coherency matrix representation of the field with the density matrix of quantum statistical mechanics. They applied the coherency matrix formalism to certain specific optical instruments by deriving the transformation law in the quasimonochromatic case for the coherency matrix in terms of the instrument operators.

In the context of this very brief survey, we shall now consider in some detail the various methods outlined above. In doing this, we propose to bring these methods into one framework. (We mention that a similar approach was also taken by N. G. Parke III [10].) Thus, we shall start with the analytic signal representation of the field introduced earlier in Chapter 8. We write the x- and y-components of the field in the form

$$E_x(\mathbf{x}, t) = E_x^{(r)}(\mathbf{x}, t) + iE_x^{(i)}(\mathbf{x}, t),$$

and

$$E_y(\mathbf{x}, t) = E_y^{(r)}(\mathbf{x}, t) + iE_y^{(i)}(\mathbf{x}, t),$$

for a typical point $\mathbf{x}$ in the field at time t. In general, instruments are frequency dependent. They will introduce different effects on different Fourier frequency components of the field. But we shall restrict ourselves to the quasimonochromatic approximation. Then it can be shown (Wolf [8]) that the effect of the instrument is the same as if the x- and y-components of the field were themselves affected by the same amount as the *mean* Fourier frequency component. Thus in this approximation all frequency dependent quantities may be evaluated at the mean frequency $\bar{\nu}$, and furthermore, we may operate directly on the x- and y-components of the field instead of the respective Fourier frequency components separately.

In Section 9–2, the Jones method is discussed by way of illustration. In Section 9–3 the coherency matrix formalism is introduced. The Mueller method is then discussed in Section 9–4 with reference to the notion of the Poincaré sphere. Finally, in Section 9–5, we consider some special topics of interest.

9–2 Jones method

As remarked earlier we consider here purely monochromatic (hence fully polarized) fields. We associate, (Fig. 9–1) with the incoming monochromatic plane wave field, a two component column vector $\boldsymbol{\varepsilon}$,

$$\boldsymbol{\varepsilon} = \begin{bmatrix} E_x \\ E_y \end{bmatrix}, \tag{9–1}$$

where E_x and E_y are time harmonic. That is, their time dependence is of the form exp $(-i2\pi\nu t)$, where ν is the frequency. We point out that the real and imaginary parts of this representation are Hilbert conjugate, and hence it is an analytic signal. (Thus the analytic signal is a natural generalization of the representation that has long been used in relation to monochromatic fields.)

We shall denote the instrument operator by **L** which has the form,

$$\mathbf{L} = \begin{bmatrix} a & b \\ c & d \end{bmatrix}, \tag{9-2}$$

where a, b, etc. are its possible matrix elements. The outgoing field is then easily obtained by matrix multiplication,

$$\mathbf{\varepsilon'} = \mathbf{L\varepsilon}. \tag{9-3}$$

EXAMPLE. Consider a plane polarized collimated beam of light, with the plane of polarization making an angle of 45° to the x-axis, incident on a compensator ($\lambda/4$ plate) with its slow axis in the x-direction. We wish to obtain the polarization characteristics of the outgoing beam of light.

First, according to Eq. (9-1) we associate a two-component column vector with the incoming beam,

$$\mathbf{\varepsilon} = a \begin{bmatrix} 1 \\ 1 \end{bmatrix},$$

where, in the constant a, we absorb the amplitude and the time harmonic factor exp $(-i2\pi\nu t)$. Now the compensator will not mix the x- and y-components of the field, hence the matrix operator **L** [Eq. (9-2)] must be diagonal. Furthermore, it changes only the relative phase difference between the field components. Therefore we have

$$\mathbf{L} = \begin{bmatrix} e^{i2\delta} & 0 \\ 0 & 1 \end{bmatrix} \quad \text{or} \quad \mathbf{L} = \begin{bmatrix} e^{i\delta} & 0 \\ 0 & e^{-i\delta} \end{bmatrix}. \tag{9-4}$$

We shall choose the latter form for reasons of symmetry. Such a compensator will introduce a relative phase difference of 2δ in the x- and y-components. In particular when $\delta = \pi/4$, **L** represents a quarter wave plate, and we have, according to the transformation law [Eq. (9-3)],

$$\mathbf{\varepsilon'} = ae^{i\pi/4} \begin{bmatrix} 1 \\ -i \end{bmatrix}$$

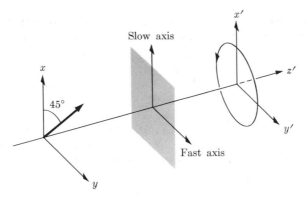

FIGURE 9–2

as the representation of the outgoing field Fig. 9–2. The two-component vector $\mathbf{\mathcal{E}}'$ clearly shows that the y-component is retarded in phase by $\pi/2$ relative to the x-component. Hence the outgoing field is right* circularly polarized. The total intensity for the incoming and the outgoing field is easily seen to be

$$I = |E_x|^2 + |E_y|^2 = |E_x'|^2 + |E_y'|^2 = 2|a|^2. \tag{9-5}$$

For N-instruments in cascade, we simply multiply the N-operators $(\mathbf{L}_N \mathbf{L}_{N-1} \ldots \mathbf{L}_2 \mathbf{L}_1)$ to get a combined operator matrix $\mathbf{L}$ for the system. The outgoing field is easily obtained by using Eq. (9–3). This is indeed a very simple and elegant approach. In reality, of course, monochromatic (fully polarized) wave fields are mathematical idealizations. In considering the more realistic quasimonochromatic approximation to the radiation field, we first observe that the two component representation Eq. (9–1) of the field is not adequate to study partially polarized (or in the extreme case unpolarized) wave fields. It is therefore necessary to go to a *higher-order* representation of the field. We give one such possibility in the next section.

9–3 The coherency matrix formalism

By way of example, we first consider (natural) unpolarized quasimonochromatic radiation field. By unpolarized, we mean that the position of the electric vector is indeterminate. That is, it is equally likely to be anywhere in the xy-plane. Consequently, its projection on the x-axis, on a

---

* For an observer looking in the direction in which the light is coming, the field is customarily called right circularly polarized if the tip of the electric vector describes a circle in the clockwise sense. (Born and Wolf [11], p. 27.)

long time average basis, will be as many times positive as negative; similarly for the y-projection. Hence, in a sufficiently long time average, we may expect that

$$\langle E_x \rangle = 0,$$

$$\langle E_y \rangle = 0,$$

(9–6)

where $\langle \cdots \rangle$ stand for time average. However, the intensity in the x- or y-component is always positive so that the time average intensity is not zero. On the average, we may expect the intensity in the x- and y-components to be equal, i.e.,

$$\langle E_x E_x^* \rangle = \langle E_y E_y^* \rangle.$$

(9–7)

Furthermore, the x- and y-components in our present example are uncorrelated, and hence on the average

$$\langle E_x E_y^* \rangle = 0 = \langle E_y E_x^* \rangle,$$

(9–8)

because they have zero mean. [See Eq. (9–6).] It is convenient to regard the correlation functions considered in Eqs. (9–7) and (9–8) as the elements of a 2×2 matrix, and write

$$\tfrac{1}{2} I \begin{bmatrix} 1 & 0 \\ 0 & 1 \end{bmatrix},$$

(9–9)

where I is the total intensity; i.e.

$$I = \langle E_x E_x^* \rangle + \langle E_y E_y^* \rangle.$$

The matrix in Eq. (9–9) is called the coherency matrix representation of the unpolarized radiation field, it is simply a constant multiple of the unit matrix.

We now formulate mathematically the coherency matrix representation of the (quasimonochromatic) radiation field. Consider a quasimonochromatic light wave of mean frequency $\bar{\nu}$ propagating in the positive z-direction. Let

$$E_x(t) = a_1(t) \exp \left[i \{ \phi_1(t) - 2\pi\bar{\nu}t \} \right],$$

$$E_y(t) = a_2(t) \exp \left[i \{ \phi_2(t) - 2\pi\bar{\nu}t \} \right]$$

(9–10)

represent two mutually orthogonal components at a typical point **x** in the field at time t (see Born and Wolf [11], p. 541). Following‡ Parent and

---

‡ We depart from Wolf's original definition of the coherency matrix merely for the sake of uniformity here.

Roman [9], we now define the coherency matrix $\mathbf{J}$ by the direct product,

$$\mathbf{J} = \langle \boldsymbol{\varepsilon} \times \boldsymbol{\varepsilon}^\dagger \rangle = \begin{bmatrix} \langle E_x E_x^* \rangle & \langle E_x E_y^* \rangle \\ \langle E_y E_x^* \rangle & \langle E_y E_y^* \rangle \end{bmatrix} \equiv \begin{bmatrix} J_{xx} & J_{xy} \\ J_{yx} & J_{xx} \end{bmatrix}. \qquad (9\text{–}11)$$

Here the elements E_x, E_y of the two-component column vector $\boldsymbol{\varepsilon}$ are as given in Eq. (9–10). The matrix $\boldsymbol{\varepsilon}^\dagger$ is the Hermitian conjugate of $\boldsymbol{\varepsilon}$, i.e. the row matrix

$$\boldsymbol{\varepsilon}^\dagger = [E_x^* \quad E_y^*].$$

The $\times$ signifies the Kronecker product (direct product) of $\boldsymbol{\varepsilon}$ and $\boldsymbol{\varepsilon}^\dagger$ in Eq. (9–11), while $\langle \cdots \rangle$, as before, stands for the time average.

When such a beam of light passes through an instrument whose matrix is denoted by $\mathbf{L}$, we first observe that

$$\boldsymbol{\varepsilon}' = \mathbf{L}\boldsymbol{\varepsilon}, \qquad (9\text{–}12)$$

and so the coherency matrix representation $\mathbf{J}'$ of the outgoing beam is

$$\mathbf{J}' = \langle \boldsymbol{\varepsilon}' \times \boldsymbol{\varepsilon}'^\dagger \rangle = \langle \mathbf{L}\boldsymbol{\varepsilon} \times \boldsymbol{\varepsilon}^\dagger \mathbf{L}^\dagger \rangle,$$

or making use of Eq. (9–11), we have

$$\mathbf{J}' = \mathbf{L}\mathbf{J}\mathbf{L}^\dagger. \qquad (9\text{–}13)$$

This is the transformation law for the coherency matrix in the quasi-monochromatic approximation.

At this point it will be instructive to study the example considered in Section 9–2 in terms of the coherency matrix. In this particular example the operation of the time average in defining the coherency matrix Eq. (9–11) may be omitted, since the field incident on the quarter wave plate is purely monochromatic. Following the definition [Eq. (9–11)], the coherency matrix for the incident beam is found to be,

$$\mathbf{J} = |a|^2 \begin{bmatrix} 1 & 1 \\ 1 & 1 \end{bmatrix}. \qquad (9\text{–}14)$$

The matrix $\mathbf{L}$ for the compensator is that given in Eq. (9–4) for $\delta = +\pi/4$. Using the transformation law Eq. (9–13), we obtain the coherency matrix for the outgoing field. We find

$$\mathbf{J}' = \mathbf{L}\mathbf{J}\mathbf{L}^\dagger = \begin{bmatrix} e^{i\pi/4} & 0 \\ 0 & e^{-i\pi/4} \end{bmatrix} |a|^2 \begin{bmatrix} 1 & 1 \\ 1 & 1 \end{bmatrix} \begin{bmatrix} e^{-i\pi/4} & 0 \\ 0 & e^{+i\pi/4} \end{bmatrix}$$

$$= |a|^2 \begin{bmatrix} 1 & +i \\ -i & 1 \end{bmatrix}, \qquad (9\text{–}15)$$

as the coherency matrix for right circularly polarized radiation field.

The total intensity in the field is given simply by the trace of the coherency matrix,

$$I = \text{Tr } \mathbf{J} = J_{xx} + J_{yy}.$$

For the particular example just studied the total intensity is

$$I = 2|a|^2,$$

for both the incoming and the outgoing beams as in Eq. (9–5).

The degree of polarization P may be defined as the ratio of the intensity of the polarized part I_{pol} of the radiation to the total intensity I_{tot}; i.e.,

$$P = \frac{I_{\text{pol}}}{I_{\text{tot}}}.$$

For the details of the calculation, we refer the reader to Born and Wolf [11], p. 548. In analogy with the theory of partial coherence, we may define the normalized cross-correlation function μ_{xy} as

$$\mu_{xy} = \frac{J_{xy}}{\sqrt{J_{xx}}\sqrt{J_{yy}}}$$

(by Schwarz's inequality, it can be shown that $|\mu_{xy}| \leq 1$). In other words, we have regarded the field under consideration as a *coherent* superposition of two fields, one fully polarized in the x-direction and the other in the y-direction. As Parrent and Roman [19] have shown, the degree of polarization may then be defined as the maximum modulus of μ_{xy} with respect to the rotation of the chosen coordinate system about the z-axis. The formula [8] for the degree of polarization, so obtained, is

$$P = +\sqrt{1 - [4 \det \mathbf{J}/(\text{Tr } \mathbf{J})^2]}, \tag{9–16}$$

where $\det \mathbf{J}$ is the determinant value of the coherency matrix $\mathbf{J}$. The expression for P is rotationally invariant, since $\det \mathbf{J}$ and $\text{Tr } \mathbf{J}$ are themselves independent of the particular choice of the x- and y-axes. We observe that the degree of polarization is zero for natural radiation, according to the coherency matrix in Eq. (9–9). On the other hand, $P = +1$ for the coherency matrices in Eqs. (9–14) and (9–15) which represent monochromatic wave fields. By the alternative definition of P as the maximum modulus of μ_{xy}, it is seen that $0 \leq P \leq 1$.

Before closing this section we remark that the coherency matrix representation of the partially polarized wave field is Hermitian. The matrix $\mathbf{J}$ is 2×2 and hence contains only four independent real parameters. These four parameters can be determined by experiment and are sufficient to

specify the field. We first note that the intensity is the observable parameter in any experiment. The intensity I' of the outgoing beam can be found
from the transformation law [Eq. (9–13)],

$$I' = \operatorname{Tr} \mathbf{J}' = \operatorname{Tr}[\mathbf{LJL}^\dagger] = \operatorname{Tr}[(\mathbf{L}^\dagger \mathbf{L})\mathbf{J}]. \qquad (9\text{–}17)$$

Let us consider an example of a polarizer, such as a Nicol prism, which
passes only a particular component of the field, say the component making
an angle θ with the x-direction. Thus a Nicol prism may be represented as
a projection operator,

$$\mathbf{P}(\theta) = \begin{bmatrix} \cos^2\theta & \sin\theta\cos\theta \\ \sin\theta\cos\theta & \sin^2\theta \end{bmatrix}, \qquad (9\text{–}18)$$

which is Hermitian and takes the projection of the $\boldsymbol{\varepsilon}$-field in the θ-direction.
Projection operators satisfy the idempotency condition

$$\mathbf{P}(\theta)\mathbf{P}(\theta) = \mathbf{P}(\theta).$$

If natural unpolarized radiation [Eq. (9–9)] is incident on a Nicol prism,
the intensity I' of the outgoing field is found by using Eq. (9–17). The
result is

$$I' = \operatorname{Tr}[\mathbf{PJP}] = \operatorname{Tr}[\mathbf{PJ}] = \tfrac{1}{2}I.$$

Thus only half the original intensity is transmitted.

Now consider an arbitrary beam whose coherency matrix is similar to
that given in Eq. (9–11). When this is incident on a polarizer which is
oriented in such a way that $\theta = 0$, we get,

$$I' = \operatorname{Tr}[\mathbf{P}(0)\mathbf{J}] = J_{xx}. \qquad (9\text{–}19)$$

The measurement of this intensity thus gives us the value of the parameter
J_{xx} in Eq. (9–11); similarly, for the y-component,

$$I' = \operatorname{Tr}\left[\mathbf{P}\left(\frac{\pi}{2}\right)\mathbf{J}\right] = J_{yy}. \qquad (9\text{–}20)$$

Further, it can be easily verified that

$$I' = \operatorname{Tr}\left[\mathbf{P}\left(\frac{\pi}{4}\right)\mathbf{J}\right]$$
$$= \tfrac{1}{2}[J_{xx} + J_{yy} + \{J_{yx} + J_{xy}\}]. \qquad (9\text{–}21)$$

Furthermore, if we consider a cascade of instruments

$$\left\{\mathbf{C}\left(+\frac{\pi}{4}\right)\mathbf{P}\left(\frac{\pi}{4}\right)\mathbf{C}\left(-\frac{\pi}{4}\right)\right\},$$

where $\mathbf{C}$ is the compensator [Eq. (9–4)], it is possible to show that,

$$I' = \operatorname{Tr}\left[\left\{\mathbf{C}\left(+\frac{\pi}{4}\right)\mathbf{P}\left(\frac{\pi}{4}\right)\mathbf{C}\left(-\frac{\pi}{4}\right)\right\}J\right]$$
$$= \tfrac{1}{2}[J_{xx} + J_{yy} + i(J_{yx} - J_{xy})]. \tag{9–22}$$

In this last expression, the operator $\mathbf{C}(-\pi/4)$ is the same as the compensator $\mathbf{C}(+\pi/4)$ rotated through $\pi/2$ about the z-axis (see Marathay [12]). That is, the fast and the slow axes of the compensator are interchanged. Thus we see from Eqs. (9–19) through (9–21) that only four intensity measurements are necessary to determine the four parameters J_{xx}, J_{yy}, ReJ_{xy}, and ImJ_{xy} of the coherency matrix. We mention that there are other ways in which the measurement of the elements of the coherency matrix can be carried out, but we have given only one such procedure.

Thus in the coherency matrix formalism, the state of the field and the instrument operator are both 2×2 matrices, in general, having complex elements. In the following section, we give an alternative description of the problem, known as the Mueller method, in which the state of the field is specified by a column vector (Stokes vector) having real components, and the instrument operator is specified as a 4×4 matrix (Mueller matrix) with all its elements real.

9–4 The Stokes parameters and the Mueller method

For convenience, and to maintain uniformity, we again start with the elements of the coherency matrix. This time, we define a column vector by the formula

$$\mathcal{J} = \langle \boldsymbol{\varepsilon} \times \boldsymbol{\varepsilon}^* \rangle = \begin{bmatrix} J_{xx} \\ J_{xy} \\ J_{yx} \\ J_{yy} \end{bmatrix}, \tag{9–23}$$

where * denotes complex conjugate. The elements of $\mathcal{J}$ in Eq. (9–23) are, in fact, the same as the elements of the coherency matrix. A further advantage is gained by making a suitable unitary transformation in this four-dimensional space such that the new elements are all real. We have

$$\mathbf{S} = \mathbf{T}\mathcal{J}, \tag{9–24}$$

where $\mathbf{T}$ is the unitary† transformation.

---

† We mention that the matrix $\mathbf{T}$ is not quite unitary because a constant factor $1/\sqrt{2}$ has been omitted. This is done so that the definition of the Stokes parameters as given in Eq. (9–25) will coincide with the customary definition (Stokes, 1852).

Writing this out, we get

$$
\begin{bmatrix} S_0 \\ S_1 \\ S_2 \\ S_3 \end{bmatrix} = \begin{bmatrix} 1 & 0 & 0 & 1 \\ 1 & 0 & 0 & -1 \\ 0 & 1 & 1 & 0 \\ 0 & -i & i & 0 \end{bmatrix} \begin{bmatrix} J_{xx} \\ J_{xy} \\ J_{yx} \\ J_{yy} \end{bmatrix}. \tag{9-25}
$$

The new elements so defined are called the *Stokes parameters* and are all real. Like the coherency matrix, the four Stokes parameters are sufficient to specify the state of the field.

We now find the transformation law for the Stokes parameters as the light passes through a physical device. We recall the relation [Eq. (9–12)] and observe that

$$ \mathcal{J}' = \langle \mathcal{E}' \times \mathcal{E}'^* \rangle = \langle \mathbf{L}\mathcal{E} \times \mathbf{L}^*\mathcal{E}^* \rangle \quad \text{or} \quad \mathcal{J}' = (\mathbf{L} \times \mathbf{L}^*)\mathcal{J}. $$

In the last step, we have made use of the relation

$$ (\mathbf{AA}' \times \mathbf{BB}') = (\mathbf{A} \times \mathbf{B})(\mathbf{A}' \times \mathbf{B}'), $$

where $\mathbf{A}$, $\mathbf{A}'$ etc. are matrices; and the $\times$ stands for their Kronecker product. Further, making use of the transformation matrix $\mathbf{T}$ of Eq. (9–24), we easily find that

$$ \mathbf{S}' = \mathbf{T}\mathcal{J}' = \mathbf{T}(\mathbf{L} \times \mathbf{L}^*)\mathbf{T}^{-1}\mathbf{T}\mathcal{J} = [\mathbf{T}(\mathbf{L} \times \mathbf{L}^*)\mathbf{T}^{-1}]\mathbf{S}, $$

or defining the Mueller matrix $\mathbf{M}$ by

$$ \mathbf{M} = \mathbf{T}(\mathbf{L} \times \mathbf{L}^*)\mathbf{T}^{-1}, \tag{9-26} $$

we have

$$ \mathbf{S}' = \mathbf{MS}. $$

We leave, for the interested reader, the solution of the example given in Section 9–2, by using the Mueller method. We mention only that the Mueller matrix $\mathbf{C}_M(\delta)$ for a compensator $\mathbf{C}(\delta)$,

$$ \mathbf{C}(\delta) = \begin{bmatrix} e^{i\delta} & 0 \\ 0 & e^{-i\delta} \end{bmatrix}, \tag{9-27} $$

can be constructed by using Eq. (9–26). In fact, we find that

$$ \mathbf{C}_M(\delta) = \begin{bmatrix} 1 & 0 & 0 & 0 \\ 0 & 1 & 0 & 0 \\ 0 & 0 & \cos 2\delta & -\sin 2\delta \\ 0 & 0 & \sin 2\delta & \cos 2\delta \end{bmatrix}. \tag{9-28} $$

TABLE 9–1

State of polarization	ε	$\mathbf{J}$	$\mathbf{S}$
Plane of polarization in the x-direction	$\begin{bmatrix} 1 \\ 0 \end{bmatrix}$	$\begin{bmatrix} 1 & 0 \\ 0 & 0 \end{bmatrix}$	$\begin{bmatrix} 1 \\ 1 \\ 0 \\ 0 \end{bmatrix}$
Plane of polarization in the y-direction	$\begin{bmatrix} 0 \\ 1 \end{bmatrix}$	$\begin{bmatrix} 0 & 0 \\ 0 & 1 \end{bmatrix}$	$\begin{bmatrix} 1 \\ -1 \\ 0 \\ 0 \end{bmatrix}$
Plane of polarization at 45° to the x-axis	$\begin{bmatrix} 1 \\ 1 \end{bmatrix}$	$\begin{bmatrix} 1 & 1 \\ 1 & 1 \end{bmatrix}$	$\begin{bmatrix} 1 \\ 0 \\ 1 \\ 0 \end{bmatrix}$
Plane of polarization at 135° to the x-axis	$\begin{bmatrix} 1 \\ -1 \end{bmatrix}$	$\begin{bmatrix} 1 & -1 \\ -1 & 1 \end{bmatrix}$	$\begin{bmatrix} 1 \\ 0 \\ -1 \\ 0 \end{bmatrix}$
Right circular polarization	$\begin{bmatrix} 1 \\ -i \end{bmatrix}$	$\begin{bmatrix} 1 & i \\ -i & 1 \end{bmatrix}$	$\begin{bmatrix} 1 \\ 0 \\ 0 \\ 1 \end{bmatrix}$
Left circular polarization	$\begin{bmatrix} 1 \\ i \end{bmatrix}$	$\begin{bmatrix} 1 & -i \\ i & +1 \end{bmatrix}$	$\begin{bmatrix} 1 \\ 0 \\ 0 \\ -1 \end{bmatrix}$

For ease of comparison, we give, in Table 9–1, the Jones vector ε, the coherency matrix $\mathbf{J}$ and the Stokes vector $\mathbf{S}$ for special cases of purely monochromatic wave fields in definite states of polarization. In Table 9–1, we have omitted the normalization factors solely for convenience of tabulation.

In the Stokes parametric representation of the field, the total intensity is given by S_0, since from Eq. (9–25), we find $S_0 = J_{xx} + J_{yy}$. The degree of polarization P can be defined in terms of the Stokes parameters. We simply substitute from Eq. (9–25) into Eq. (9–16) and obtain

$$P = + \frac{\sqrt{S_1^2 + S_2^2 + S_3^2}}{S_0}. \tag{9–29}$$

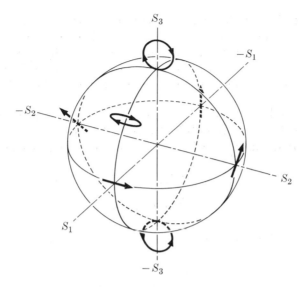

FIGURE 9–3

For the measurement of Stokes parameters, we follow the procedure outlined in Section 9–3. Since the Stokes parameters are linearly related to the elements of the coherency matrix through relation Eq. (9–25), the proper linear combinations of the four intensity measurements in Eqs. (9–19) through (9–22) enable us to determine the Stokes parameters.

For a fully polarized wave field $P = +1$, and the definition of the degree of polarization [Eq. (9–29)] gives,

$$S_0^2 = S_1^2 + S_2^2 + S_3^2.$$

This is an equation of a sphere (in the Stokes subspace S_1, S_2, S_3) whose radius is S_0, the total intensity; this is called the Poincaré sphere.* For partially polarized wave fields, the radius of the sphere is Ps_0, and for unpolarized (natural) radiation, the sphere shrinks to zero radius. Each point on this sphere corresponds to definite values of the parameters S_1, S_2, S_3, and hence to a definite state of polarization. In Fig. 9–3, we show a unit sphere in the Stokes subspace (S_1, S_2, S_3). On this sphere we symbolically depict the states of polarization listed in Table 9–1.

In the example considered in Section 9–2, we see that the representative point on the Poincaré sphere for the incident beam has coordinates $(0, +S_2, 0)$. After passage through the compensator ($\lambda/4$ plate), the outgoing beam was found to be right circularly polarized. In other words,

---

* Conventionally, the Poincaré sphere is constructed with unit radius, and the polarization states are studied without reference to the total intensity.

as remarked in the introduction (Section 9–1), the representative point has moved, on the Poincaré sphere, to a new position whose coordinates are $(0, 0, +S_3)$. It is evident that a compensator with its slow axis in the x-direction causes a rotation about the S_1-axis in the Stokes subspace. This rotation is also evident from the form of the Mueller matrix $\mathbf{C}_M$ in Eq. (9–28).

For another example of such a rotation in the Stokes subspace, we consider a rotator $\mathbf{R}(\theta)$. A rotator is a physical device which causes a rotation of the plane of polarization. The matrix representation of such a rotator is

$$\mathbf{R}(\theta) = \begin{bmatrix} \cos\theta & -\sin\theta \\ \sin\theta & \cos\theta \end{bmatrix}. \tag{9–30}$$

The corresponding Mueller matrix $\mathbf{R}_M$ can be obtained by using Eq. (9–26); it is

$$\mathbf{R}_M = \begin{bmatrix} 1 & 0 & 0 & 0 \\ 0 & \cos 2\theta & -\sin 2\theta & 0 \\ 0 & \sin 2\theta & \cos 2\theta & 0 \\ 0 & 0 & 0 & 1 \end{bmatrix}.$$

Thus a rotation of the plane of polarization about the z-axis through an angle θ induces a rotation about the S_3-axis through 2θ in the Stokes subspace. For further details of this remarkable property of the Poincaré sphere (or rather the Stokes subspace) we refer the reader to Marathay [12].

Before closing this section we give the representations of certain familiar optical instruments in Table 9–2, for ready reference.

Having thus familiarized ourselves with these methods of dealing with the problems concerned with polarized or partially polarized light, we shall now turn our attention to some special topics of interest.

9–5 Selected topics

(a) *Probabilistic interpretation of the eigenvalues of* $\mathbf{J}$. The coherency matrix $\mathbf{J}$ [Eq. (9–11)] is Hermitian, and hence a suitable unitary matrix can always be found to diagonalize it. Its eigenvalues λ_1 and λ_2 are obtained by solving the characteristic equation. They are found to be

$$\lambda_1 = \tfrac{1}{2} \operatorname{Tr} \mathbf{J} \left[1 + \sqrt{1 - \frac{4 \det \mathbf{J}}{(\operatorname{Tr} \mathbf{J})^2}} \right],$$

$$\lambda_2 = \tfrac{1}{2} \operatorname{Tr} \mathbf{J} \left[1 - \sqrt{1 - \frac{4 \det \mathbf{J}}{(\operatorname{Tr} \mathbf{J})^2}} \right].$$

TABLE 9–2

THE 2×2 AND THE MUELLER MATRIX REPRESENTATIONS OF CERTAIN OPTICAL INSTRUMENTS

Instrument	2×2 representation	Mueller matrix
Compensator: Introduces a relative phase difference of 2δ	$\mathbf{C}(\delta) = \begin{bmatrix} e^{i\delta} & 0 \\ 0 & e^{-i\delta} \end{bmatrix}$	$\mathbf{C}_M(\delta) = \begin{bmatrix} 1 & 0 & 0 & 0 \\ 0 & 1 & 0 & 0 \\ 0 & 0 & \cos 2\delta & -\sin 2\delta \\ 0 & 0 & \sin 2\delta & \cos 2\delta \end{bmatrix}$
Rotator: Rotates the plane of polarization counterclockwise through angle θ about the z-axis	$\mathbf{R}(\theta) = \begin{bmatrix} \cos\theta & -\sin\theta \\ \sin\theta & \cos\theta \end{bmatrix}$	$\mathbf{R}_M(\theta) = \begin{bmatrix} 1 & 0 & 0 & 0 \\ 0 & \cos 2\theta & -\sin 2\theta & 0 \\ 0 & \sin 2\theta & \cos 2\theta & 0 \\ 0 & 0 & 0 & 1 \end{bmatrix}$
Polarizer: Takes the projection of the $\mathcal{E}$ field in the direction making an angle α with the x-axis	$\mathbf{P}(\alpha) = \begin{bmatrix} \cos^2\alpha & \sin\alpha\cos\alpha \\ \sin\alpha\cos\alpha & \sin^2\alpha \end{bmatrix}$	$\mathbf{P}_M(\alpha) = \frac{1}{2}\begin{bmatrix} 1 & \cos 2\alpha & \sin 2\alpha & 0 \\ \cos 2\alpha & \cos^2 2\alpha & \sin 2\alpha\cos 2\alpha & 0 \\ \sin 2\alpha & \sin 2\alpha\cos 2\alpha & \sin^2 2\alpha & 0 \\ 0 & 0 & 0 & 0 \end{bmatrix}$
Absorber: η_x, η_y are the absorption coefficients in the x- and y-directions	$\mathbf{A} = \begin{bmatrix} e^{-\eta_x} & 0 \\ 0 & e^{-\eta_y} \end{bmatrix}$ $= e^{-\bar\eta}\begin{bmatrix} e^{-\epsilon} & 0 \\ 0 & e^{+\epsilon} \end{bmatrix}$	$\mathbf{A}_M = e^{-2\bar\eta}\begin{bmatrix} \cosh 2\epsilon & -\sinh 2\epsilon & 0 & 0 \\ -\sinh 2\epsilon & \cosh 2\epsilon & 0 & 0 \\ 0 & 0 & 1 & 0 \\ 0 & 0 & 0 & 1 \end{bmatrix}$
Define the mean absorption coefficient by $\bar\eta = \frac{1}{2}(\eta_x + \eta_y)$ and mean difference by $\epsilon = \frac{1}{2}(\eta_x - \eta_y)$		

When diagonalized, the coherency matrix has the form

$$\mathbf{J}_D = \begin{bmatrix} \lambda_1 & 0 \\ 0 & \lambda_2 \end{bmatrix}. \tag{9-31}$$

In this section, we first propose to give a possible probabilistic interpretation of the eigenvalues of the coherency matrix given in Eq. (9-31). The diagonalized coherency matrix in Eq. (9-31) may be rewritten in the form

$$\frac{1}{\lambda_1 + \lambda_2} \mathbf{J}_D = \frac{1}{\lambda_1 + \lambda_2} \begin{bmatrix} \lambda_1 & 0 \\ 0 & 0 \end{bmatrix} + \frac{1}{\lambda_1 + \lambda_2} \begin{bmatrix} 0 & 0 \\ 0 & \lambda_2 \end{bmatrix} \tag{9-32}$$

$$\equiv \mathbf{J}_D^{(1)} + \mathbf{J}_D^{(2)}.$$

Presented in this form the original *partially* polarized beam whose coherency matrix is $\mathbf{J}_D$ may be regarded as made up of an *incoherent* superposition of two independent *fully polarized* beams of relative intensities λ_1 and λ_2. Beam 1 whose coherency matrix is $\mathbf{J}_D^{(1)}$ is fully polarized in the x-direction, and beam 2 is polarized in the y-direction, with the coherency matrix $\mathbf{J}_D^{(2)}$.

To give a probabilistic interpretation of the eigenvalues λ_1 and λ_2, let us consider a projection operator whose eigenstates are the x- and y-states of polarization. (We have made this particular choice of the projection operator because the coherency matrix is in terms of the x- and y-components of the field.) Clearly, a polarizer [Eq. (9-18)] (Nicol prism) with the orientation $\theta = 0$, or $\theta = \pi/2$ is such an instrument. Let us suppose that a polarizer $\mathbf{P}(0)$ [Eq. (9-18)] is interposed in the path of the beam described by the coherency matrix in Eq. (9-32). We note that the intensity and the state of polarization are two independent properties of the beam. Now suppose the intensity is reduced to such an extent that on the average there is only one "photon" in transit from the source to the polarizer $\mathbf{P}(0)$. The probability that this photon will go through the polarizer $\mathbf{P}(0)$, which admits only the x-state of linear polarization, is clearly $\lambda_1/(\lambda_1 + \lambda_2)$. On the other hand, the probability that no photon will be received is $\lambda_2/(\lambda_1 + \lambda_2)$. Similar considerations apply to a polarizer oriented at $\theta = \pi/2$.

One might ask, what about the probabilistic interpretation of the eigenvalues when the polarizer is oriented at an arbitrary angle θ which is neither 0 nor $\pi/2$? To answer this question, we must first conform with the rules of the game in quantum mechanics and describe the state of the field as a linear combination of the eigenstates of the polarizer $\mathbf{P}(\theta)$, Eq. (9-18). We have already shown in Eq. (9-32) that the original beam may be regarded as an incoherent superposition of two *fully polarized* beams whose coherency matrices are $\mathbf{J}_D^{(1)}$ and $\mathbf{J}_D^{(2)}$. For a fully polarized beam 1, for example, we may write the Jones vector in the form

$$\sqrt{\frac{\lambda_1}{\lambda_1 + \lambda_2}}\begin{bmatrix} 1 \\ 0 \end{bmatrix}.$$

This may be expanded as a linear combination of the eigenstates of $\mathbf{P}(\theta)$, thus,

$$\sqrt{\frac{\lambda_1}{\lambda_1 + \lambda_2}}\begin{bmatrix} 1 \\ 0 \end{bmatrix} = \sqrt{\frac{\lambda_1}{\lambda_1 + \lambda_2}}\cos\theta\begin{bmatrix} \cos\theta \\ -\sin\theta \end{bmatrix} + \sqrt{\frac{\lambda_1}{\lambda_1 + \lambda_2}}\sin\theta\begin{bmatrix} \sin\theta \\ \cos\theta \end{bmatrix}.$$

$$(9\text{--}33)$$

Here

$$\begin{bmatrix} \cos\theta \\ -\sin\theta \end{bmatrix} \quad \text{and} \quad \begin{bmatrix} \sin\theta \\ \cos\theta \end{bmatrix}$$

are the normalized orthogonal eigenstates of $\mathbf{P}(\theta)$ with the eigenvalues $+1$ and 0, respectively. It is important to note here that the instrument $\mathbf{P}(\theta)$ interprets the state of polarization of beam 1 as a superposition of its *own* eigenstates. So that the probability that a "photon" will be received through $\mathbf{P}(\theta)$ may be obtained by again appealing to the methods of quantum mechanics. This probability is the squared modulus of the expansion coefficient in Eq. (9–33) of the state

$$\begin{bmatrix} \cos\theta \\ -\sin\theta \end{bmatrix}$$

which is admitted by the polarizer $\mathbf{P}(\theta)$. When a photon with the probability $(\lambda_1 \cos^2\theta)/(\lambda_1 + \lambda_2)$ is received, it is certain to be in the state

$$\begin{bmatrix} \cos\theta \\ -\sin\theta \end{bmatrix}.$$

Similar considerations apply for beam 2. We first write,

$$\sqrt{\frac{\lambda_2}{\lambda_1 + \lambda_2}}\begin{bmatrix} 0 \\ 1 \end{bmatrix} = -\sqrt{\frac{\lambda_2}{\lambda_1 + \lambda_2}}\sin\theta\begin{bmatrix} \cos\theta \\ -\sin\theta \end{bmatrix} + \sqrt{\frac{\lambda_2}{\lambda_1 + \lambda_2}}\cos\theta\begin{bmatrix} \sin\theta \\ \cos\theta \end{bmatrix}.$$

Then the probability that a photon is received through $\mathbf{P}(\theta)$ from beam 2 is $(\lambda_2 \sin^2\theta)/(\lambda_1 + \lambda_2)$.

Now suppose the intensity of the original beam is reduced to such an extent that, on the average, only one photon is in transit from the source to the polarizer $\mathbf{P}(\theta)$. The probability that a photon is received through

$\mathbf{P}(\theta)$ is simply the *sum* of the probabilities just computed for beams 1 and 2, namely

$$\frac{1}{\lambda_1 + \lambda_2} [\lambda_1 \cos^2 \theta + \lambda_2 \sin^2 \theta].$$

This is the case because the original partially polarized beam was made up of an *incoherent* superposition Eq. (9–32) of beam 1 and beam 2.

It is important to note that once the photon has passed through the Nicol prism, say $\mathbf{P}(\theta)$, it is then in a definite state of polarization, namely the eigenstate of $\mathbf{P}(\theta)$ for which the eigenvalue is $+1$. We shall refer to this experiment as the "preparation of the state," for if this photon were again to pass through $\mathbf{P}(\theta)$, the outcome of the experiment can be predicted with certainty. This latter experiment may be referred to as making a "measurement" on the photon. However, if the measurement is made by means of a polarizer $\mathbf{P}(\theta')$ oriented at an angle θ' different from θ, then the outcome of the experiment can only be given probabilistically, since the instrument $\mathbf{P}(\theta')$ sees the incoming photon in a superposition of its *own* eigenstates, although it was originally prepared in a definite eigenstate of $\mathbf{P}(\theta)$. This analysis also applies to any projection operator whose eigenstates are diametrically opposite on the Poincaré sphere. The discussion here was confined to projection operators merely for convenience. We leave for the interested reader the extension to Hermitian matrix representations of optical instruments which are not necessarily projection operators.

Now let us turn our attention to the "entropy" and its use in the study of partial polarization. The reader might recall that the entropy H defined by

$$H = - \sum_i p_i \log p_i,$$

in Chapter 8 describes the degree of "disorder" in the system. Recalling the probabilistic interpretations of the eigenvalues, the entropy H is found to be

$$H = - \frac{\lambda_1}{\lambda_1 + \lambda_2} \log \frac{\lambda_1}{\lambda_1 + \lambda_2} - \frac{\lambda_2}{\lambda_1 + \lambda_2} \log \frac{\lambda_2}{\lambda_1 + \lambda_2}.$$

To determine $H_{\min}$, and $H_{\max}$ subject to the condition that

$$\lambda_1 + \lambda_2 = \text{const} \equiv C, \tag{9–34}$$

it is clear, as at the end of Chapter 8, that

$$H_{\min} = 0, \quad \text{when} \quad \lambda_j = C, \quad \lambda_i = 0; \quad i \neq j; \quad i, j = 1, 2,$$

and

$$H_{\max} = \log 2 \quad \text{when} \quad \lambda_i = \frac{C}{2} \quad \text{for all} \quad i = 1, 2.$$

In the first case, only one of the eigenvalues is nonzero. Therefore, $H_{\min} = 0$ corresponds to the case of a *fully polarized* wave field. In the second case $H_{\max} = \log N$, both eigenvalues are the same, which corresponds to the case of an unpolarized wave field. It is instructive to observe that the concept of entropy is also a measure of the degree of polarization of the wave field.

(b) *The decomposition of* **J**. We have already seen in Eq. (9–32) that the diagonalized coherency matrix may be decomposed into a sum of two coherency matrices. In fact, any coherency matrix, in general,

$$\mathbf{J} = \begin{bmatrix} J_{xx} & J_{xy} \\ J_{yx} & J_{yy} \end{bmatrix},$$

may be decomposed into two parts, such as

$$\mathbf{J} = A \begin{bmatrix} 1 & 0 \\ 0 & 1 \end{bmatrix} + \begin{bmatrix} B & D \\ D^* & C \end{bmatrix}, \tag{9–35}$$

where A, B, and C are real positive quantities. Such a decomposition is not unique. However, if the extra condition,

$$BC - |D|^2 = 0,$$

is imposed, then the decomposition Eq. (9–35) is unique. Under these conditions, any partially polarized quasimonochromatic wave field may be thought of as an incoherent superposition of a completely unpolarized wave field and a fully polarized monochromatic wave field. Starting in this way, we find that the expression for the degree of polarization P [Eq. (9–16)] can be obtained as shown in Born and Wolf, p. 548.

There is another possible decomposition of the matrix **J**, namely that in terms of the Pauli spin matrices. This is so because the Pauli spin matrices are complete. They satisfy the algebra,

$$\sigma_\alpha \sigma_\beta + \sigma_\beta \sigma_\alpha = 0, \qquad \alpha, \beta = 1, 2, 3, \qquad \alpha \neq \beta$$

$$\sigma_\alpha \sigma_\beta - \sigma_\beta \sigma_\alpha = 2i\sigma_\gamma, \qquad \alpha, \beta, \gamma = 1, 2, 3, \text{ and cyclic}, \tag{9–36}$$

$$\sigma_i^2 = \sigma_0, \qquad i = 0, 1, 2, 3,$$

$$\sigma_i \sigma_0 = \sigma_0 \sigma_i = \sigma_i, \qquad i = 0, 1, 2, 3.$$

By taking the trace of the first of these relations and making use of the third relation, we can show that,

$$\mathrm{Tr}\,[\sigma_i \sigma_j] = 2\delta_{ij}, \qquad i, j = 0, 1, 2, 3. \tag{9–37}$$

For convenience, we shall use the following representation of the spin matrices,

$$\sigma_0 = \begin{bmatrix} 1 & 0 \\ 0 & 1 \end{bmatrix}, \quad \sigma_1 = \begin{bmatrix} 1 & 0 \\ 0 & -1 \end{bmatrix}, \quad \sigma_2 = \begin{bmatrix} 0 & 1 \\ 1 & 0 \end{bmatrix}, \quad \sigma_3 = \begin{bmatrix} 0 & i \\ -i & 0 \end{bmatrix}.$$

$$(9\text{--}38)$$

We mention that all the matrices in Eq. (9–38) are Hermitian.

Now any 2×2 matrix can be expanded as a linear combination of the Pauli spin matrices. The expansion coefficients are determined by using the trace condition given in Eq. (9–37). The expansion [13] of the coherency matrix $\mathbf{J}$ [Eq. (9–34)] is particularly interesting. We write

$$\mathbf{J} = \frac{1}{2} \sum_{i=0}^{3} S_i \sigma_i. \tag{9--39}$$

To determine the expansion coefficients S_i, we multiply both sides of this equation by σ_j and take the trace of both sides. Making use of Eq. (9–37), we then obtain

$$S_j = \text{Tr}\,[\mathbf{J}\sigma_j], \qquad j = 0, 1, 2, 3.$$

For example for $j = 0$, we have

$$S_0 = J_{xx} + J_{yy}.$$

In this way, the reader can verify for himself that the expansion coefficients S_i in Eq. (9–39) are in fact the Stokes parameters.

We now recall that the instrument operators in the coherency matrix formalism are all 2×2 matrices. These operators, therefore, can also be expanded in terms of the Pauli spin matrices. For example, the compensator $\mathbf{C}(\delta)$ [Eq. (9–27)] and the rotator $\mathbf{R}(\theta)$ [Eq. (9–30)] have the following Pauli expansion:

$$\mathbf{C}(\delta) = \sigma_0 \cos \delta + i\sigma_1 \sin \delta, \qquad \mathbf{R}(\theta) = \sigma_0 \cos \theta + i\sigma_3 \sin \theta. \quad (9\text{--}40)$$

It is now natural to ask what is the role played by the Pauli spin matrices as optical instruments, and what is the physical interpretation of their commutation relations Eq. (9–36)? (For details of these considerations, we refer the reader to Marathay [12].) We have already seen, in Section 9–4, that the compensator and the rotator induce rotations about the S_1-axis through 2δ and about the S_3-axis through 2θ, respectively, in the Stokes subspace (S_1, S_2, S_3). Now letting the arguments δ and θ equal $\pi/2$ in Eq. (9–40), we find that

$$\mathbf{C}(\pi/2) = i\sigma_1, \qquad \mathbf{R}(\pi/2) = i\sigma_3. \tag{9--41}$$

The constant factor $i = e^{i\pi/2}$ simply amounts to an inconsequential phase factor which leaves the relative phase difference between the x- and y-components of the field unchanged. Thus it is evident from Eq. (9–41) that the Pauli spin matrix σ_1 is a compensator that induces a rotation about the S_1-axis in the Stokes subspace, through an angle π. Similarly, the spin matrix σ_3 is a rotator that rotates the plane of polarization through $\pi/2$, about the z-axis, and induces a rotation about the S_3-axis through an angle π. We leave it for the interested reader to show that the Pauli matrix σ_2 induces a rotation about the S_2-axis. Following the form of the expressions in Eq. (9–41), an optical instrument matrix can be constructed by using the spin matrix σ_2. It can be shown that this new instrument is the same as the compensator $\mathbf{C}$, rotated about the z-axis through 45° in the counterclockwise sense, (Marathay [12]).

In the light of this interpretation, the determination of the eigenstates of σ_1 becomes trivial. Because the operator σ_1 induces a rotation about the S_1-axis, the polarization states whose representative points have coordinates $(+S_1, 0, 0)$ and $(-S_1, 0, 0)$ on the Poincaré sphere are left unchanged up to constant multiplicative factors. Therefore the x- and y-states of linear polarization are the eigenstates of σ_1. Similar considerations apply to σ_2 and σ_3.

Let us now consider the interpretation of the commutation relations of the spin matrices. First we observe that the matrices σ_j, $(j = 1, 2, 3)$ are Hermitian, but the matrices $(i\sigma_j)$ are unitary with determinant value $+1$. Now making use of the first relation in Eq. (9–36) in the second, we obtain

$$\sigma_\alpha \sigma_\beta = i\sigma_\gamma$$

or

$$(i\sigma_\alpha)(i\sigma_\beta) = -(i\sigma_\gamma). \qquad (9\text{–}42)$$

This relation clearly shows that the effect of the two instruments σ_α and σ_β in series on a quasimonochromatic (but otherwise arbitrary) beam is the same as the instrument σ_γ alone. Furthermore, Eq. (9–42) also says that a rotation about the S_β-axis through angle π followed by a rotation about the S_α-axis $(\alpha \neq \beta)$ through the same angle is equivalent to a single rotation about the third axis of the Stokes subspace through an angle π. Finally, the third relation in Eq. (9–35), namely

$$\sigma_i^2 = \sigma_0,$$

simply asserts that the double application of the operator σ_i $(i = 1, 2, 3)$ which will induce a rotation about the S_i-axis through 2π is equivalent to the operation by the unit matrix.

(c) *Interpretations of intensity measurements in the Stokes space.* The introduction of the coherency matrix in Born and Wolf, p. 542, is particularly interesting. We give only the basic argument here.

Consider an arbitrary (quasimonochromatic) beam of light whose y-component is retarded by ϵ with respect to the x-component. That is the beam passes through a compensator

$$\mathbf{C}(\epsilon) = \begin{bmatrix} e^{+i\epsilon/2} & 0 \\ 0 & e^{-i\epsilon/2} \end{bmatrix}.$$

Now the intensity $I(\theta, \epsilon)$ of the light vibrations in the direction which makes an angle θ with the x-direction can be observed by letting the beam pass through a polarizer $\mathbf{P}(\theta)$ [Eq. (9–18)]. The expression of the intensity $I(\theta, \epsilon)$ of the outgoing beam, obtained in this manner, is (Born and Wolf)

$$I(\theta, \epsilon) = J_{xx} \cos^2 \theta + J_{yy} \sin^2 \theta + J_{xy} e^{-i\epsilon} \sin \theta \cos \theta$$
$$+ J_{yx} e^{i\epsilon} \sin \theta \cos \theta, \qquad (9\text{–}43)$$

or, in more compact matrix notation, we write

$$I(\theta, \epsilon) = [\cos \theta \ \ e^{i\epsilon} \sin \theta] \begin{bmatrix} J_{xx} & J_{xy} \\ J_{yx} & J_{yy} \end{bmatrix} \begin{bmatrix} \cos \theta \\ e^{-i\epsilon} \sin \theta \end{bmatrix}$$
$$\equiv \mathbf{X}^\dagger \mathbf{J} \mathbf{X},$$

where the quantities $J_{xx}, \dots,$ etc. are the elements of the coherency matrix $\mathbf{J}$ of the *original* beam.

Now let us define an operator $\mathbf{A}$ for the two instruments $\mathbf{C}$ and $\mathbf{P}$ in series:

$$\mathbf{A} = \mathbf{P}(\theta)\mathbf{C}(\epsilon)$$
$$= \begin{bmatrix} \cos^2 \theta e^{i\epsilon/2} & \sin \theta \cos \theta e^{-i\epsilon/2} \\ \sin \theta \cos \theta e^{i\epsilon/2} & \sin^2 \theta e^{-i\epsilon/2} \end{bmatrix}.$$

The coherency matrix $\mathbf{J}'$ for the outgoing beam can then be obtained by using the transformation law [Eq. (9–13)]. We find,

$$\mathbf{J}' = \mathbf{A}\mathbf{J}\mathbf{A}^\dagger.$$

The intensity of the outgoing beam is, therefore,

$$I(\theta, \epsilon) = \text{Tr } \mathbf{J}' = \text{Tr } [\mathbf{A}\mathbf{J}\mathbf{A}^\dagger] = \text{Tr } [\mathbf{A}^\dagger \mathbf{A}\mathbf{J}].$$

Written in full, we finally have,

$$I(\theta, \epsilon) = \text{Tr} \left[\begin{pmatrix} \cos^2 \theta & e^{-i\epsilon} \sin \theta \cos \theta \\ e^{i\epsilon} \sin \theta \cos \theta & \sin^2 \theta \end{pmatrix} \begin{pmatrix} J_{xx} & J_{xy} \\ J_{yx} & J_{yy} \end{pmatrix} \right]. \qquad (9\text{–}44)$$

This expression for the observable intensity corresponding to a given instrument operator is in accordance with the general formula given by Eq. (9–17).

We propose to show, by way of illustration, that a trace relation [Eq. (9–44)] of this kind in the coherency matrix formalism for the observable intensity implies a "scalar product" of two vectors in the Stokes space. Let us expand the operator $(A^\dagger A)$ in terms of the Pauli spin matrices. We obtain

$$A^\dagger A = \sigma_0 + (\cos 2\theta)\sigma_1 + (\sin 2\theta \cos \epsilon)\sigma_2 \\ - (\sin 2\theta \sin \epsilon)\sigma_3, \qquad (9\text{–}45)$$

while the expansion of the coherency matrix in terms of the spin matrices is [Eq. (9–39)]

$$J = \tfrac{1}{2}S_0\sigma_0 + \tfrac{1}{2}S_1\sigma_1 + \tfrac{1}{2}S_2\sigma_2 + \tfrac{1}{2}S_3\sigma_3.$$

We now associate an "instrument vector," $\mathcal{C}$, with the operator $(A^\dagger A)$. The components of this four-vector according to Eq. (9–45) are 1, $\cos 2\theta$, $\sin 2\theta \cos \epsilon$, $-\sin 2\theta \sin \epsilon$. Further, we associate a Stokes four-vector with the incoming beam. The components of this four-vector $\mathbf{S}$ are $\tfrac{1}{2}S_0$, $\tfrac{1}{2}S_1$, $\tfrac{1}{2}S_2$, $\tfrac{1}{2}S_3$. The intensity of the outgoing beam is obtained by taking the scalar product of these two four-vectors,

$$I(\theta, \epsilon) = \mathcal{C} \cdot \mathbf{S}.$$

In matrix notation,

$$I(\theta, \epsilon) = \mathcal{C}^\dagger \mathbf{S} = (1 \quad \cos 2\theta \quad \sin 2\theta \cos \epsilon \quad -\sin 2\theta \sin \epsilon) \begin{pmatrix} \tfrac{1}{2}S_0 \\ \tfrac{1}{2}S_1 \\ \tfrac{1}{2}S_2 \\ \tfrac{1}{2}S_3 \end{pmatrix}.$$

That this expression leads to the correct intensity formula [Eq. (9–43)] can be easily verified by substituting the expressions for the Stokes parameters in terms of the elements of the coherency matrix, given in Eq. (9–25). Thus the intensity of the outgoing beam may be described as a scalar product of the "instrument vector" and the "Stokes vector" of the light beam.

With these remarks, we end our discussion of *classical* statistical optics. To a large extent we have confined our attention to the propagation of electromagnetic radiation and its properties. The physically more interesting problems of emission and detection must be studied by appealing to the methods of quantum theory.

References

1. G. G. STOKES, *Trans. Camb. Phil. Soc.* **9**, 399 (1852).

2. H. POINCARÉ, *Theorie Mathematique de la Lumiere* II. Paris, (1852), Chap. 12.

3. S. PANCHARANTNAM, (a) *Proc. Indian Acad. Sci.* A **44**, 398 (1956). (b) *Memoirs of the Raman Research Institute*, Banglore, India, No. 92.

4. R. C. JONES, *J. Opt. Soc. Am.* **46**, 126 (1956).

5. (a) W. A. SCHURCLIFF, *Polarized Light: Production and Use.* Harvard Univerity Press, (1962). (b) N. G. PARKE III, *J. Math. and Phys.* **28**, 2 (1949).

6. N. WIENER, "Generalized Harmonic Analysis" *Acta Math.* **55**, 118–258 (1930).

7. E. WOLF, *Nuovo Cimento* **12**, 884 (1954).

8. E. WOLF, *Nuovo Cimento* **13**, 1165–1181 (1959).

9. G. PARRENT and P. ROMAN, *Nuovo Cimento* **15**, 370–388 (1960).

10. N. G. PARKE III, *J. Math. and Phys.* **28**, 2 (1949).

11. M. BORN and E. WOLF, *Principles of Optics.* Pergamon Press (1959).

12. A. S. MARATHAY, thesis, Boston Univ., (1963).

13. U. FANO, *Phys. Rev.* **93**, 121 (1954).

14. W. H. McMASTER, *Am. J. Phys.* **22**, 351–362 (1954) *Rev. Mod. Phys.* **33**, 8–28 (1961).

15. M. J. WALKER, *Am. J. Phys.* **22**, 170–174 (1954).

Fourier-Bessel Series and Integrals

A-1 Fourier series

The decomposition of a periodic function into a sum of sinusoids is too well known [1] to reproduce in detail here. For the sake of completeness in the main text, however, we will list some of the more important forms of this decomposition.

If P represents the period (space or time),

$$f(x) = \frac{A_0}{2} + \sum_{n=1}^{\infty} (A_n \cos n\omega x + B_n \sin n\omega x) \qquad \text{(A-1)}$$

is a frequently encountered form, where $\omega = 2\pi/P$ is the angular frequency. Based on the orthogonality of the trigonometric functions over the interval $-P/2 < x < P/2$, the Fourier coefficients are given by

$$A_n = \frac{2}{P} \int_{-P/2}^{+P/2} f(x) \cos n\omega x \, dx,$$

$$B_n = \frac{2}{P} \int_{-P/2}^{+P/2} f(x) \sin n\omega x \, dx. \qquad \text{(A-2)}$$

Clearly, if $f(x)$ is an odd or even function one set of coefficients vanishes.

It is sometimes convenient to decompose $f(x)$ into a single sum, containing amplitude and phases, of the form

$$f(x) = \frac{A_0}{2} + \sum_{n=1}^{\infty} C_n \cos (n\omega x - \phi_n). \qquad \text{(A-3)}$$

To determine C_n and ϕ_n, we expand $\cos (n\omega x - \phi_n)$ into

$$\cos n\omega x \cos \phi_n + \sin n\omega x \sin \phi_n$$

and match coefficients with Eq. (A-1). The result is

$$C_n = \sqrt{A_n^2 + B_n^2},$$

$$\phi_n = \tan^{-1} \frac{B_n}{A_n}. \qquad \text{(A-4)}$$

Next, we express sin $n\omega x$ and cos $n\omega x$ as complex exponentials, substitute them into Eq. (A–1), and rearrange terms to yield

$$f(x) = \sum_{n=1}^{\infty} \frac{1}{2}(A_n + iB_n)e^{-in\omega x} + \frac{A_0}{2} + \sum_{n=1}^{\infty} \frac{1}{2}(A_n - iB_n)e^{in\omega x}. \quad \text{(A–5)}$$

It is now convenient to define

$$D_0 = \frac{A_0}{2},$$

$$D_n = \tfrac{1}{2}(A_n - iB_n), \quad \text{(A–6)}$$

$$D_{-n} = \tfrac{1}{2}(A_n + iB_n) = D_n^*$$

so that Eq. (A–5) can be cast into the compact form

$$f(x) = \sum_{n=-\infty}^{+\infty} D_n e^{in\omega x}, \quad \text{(A–7)}$$

where

$$D_n = \frac{1}{P} \int_{-P/2}^{+P/2} f(x)e^{-in\omega x}\, dx.$$

Before moving on, it should be noted that whereas A_n and B_n represent real coefficients, D_n is, in general, complex. Further, the range in the first summation in Eq. (A–5) has been shifted to include negative integers in passing to Eq. (A–7). Finally, the last step follows directly from the orthogonality condition

$$\frac{1}{P} \int_{-P/2}^{+P/2} e^{i(n-m)\omega x}\, dx = \delta_{mn}$$

or indirectly from Eq. (A–6) which incidentally can be inverted to yield A_n and B_n. As an illustration, we shall now determine the Fourier coeffi-

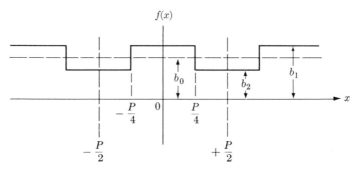

FIGURE A–1

cients for the Foucault, or black and white line, pattern often used to test optical instruments (Fig. A–1). First we note that the function is obviously even so that $B_n = 0$. Next we see that

$$\overline{f(x)} = \frac{A_0}{2} = \frac{2}{P} \int_0^{P/2} f(x)\, dx = \frac{b_1 + b_2}{2} = b_0$$

In addition

$$A_n = \frac{4}{P} \int_0^{P/4} b_1 \cos n\omega x\, dx + \frac{4}{P} \int_{P/4}^{P/2} b_2 \cos n\omega x\, dx$$

or

$$A_n = 0, \qquad n \text{ even,}$$

$$A_n = \frac{2(b_1 - b_2)}{n\pi} \sin \frac{n\pi}{2}, \qquad n \text{ odd.}$$

Now introducing the "contrast" C of the test chart as the ratio $(b_1 - b_2)/2$ to b_0, that is, the ratio of a-c to d-c, we get

$$f(x) = b_0 \left[1 + \frac{4C}{\pi} \left(\cos \omega x - \tfrac{1}{3} \cos 3\omega x + \tfrac{1}{5} \cos 5\omega x \ldots \right) \right], \qquad \text{(A–8)}$$

where

$$C = \frac{b_1 - b_2}{b_1 + b_2}.$$

A–2 Fourier integral

In passing from the Fourier series to the Fourier integral [2], it is convenient to start with the form in Eq. (A–7) and treat the nonperiodic function as periodic, and then pass to the limit $P \to \infty$. In doing so, there is some freedom in the choice of the constants appearing in the final Fourier transform relation. There are advantages and disadvantages with each school of thought in this matter. We adopt the convention here that the constants shall be chosen in such a way that the factor $1/2\pi$ appear always with $d\omega$ in frequency space.

Let us now rewrite Eq. (A–7) in the form

$$f(x) = \frac{1}{2\pi} \sum_{n=-\infty}^{\infty} \left(\frac{2\pi D n}{\omega_1} \right) e^{i n \Delta \omega x} \, \Delta \omega,$$

$$\left(\frac{2\pi D n}{\omega_1} \right) = \int_{-P/2}^{+P/2} f(x) e^{-i n \Delta \omega x} \, dx, \qquad \text{(A–9)}$$

where we have identified the fundamental frequency $\omega_1 = 2\pi/P$ with the spectral separation $\Delta \omega$. We now take the limit (assuming it exists) of these equations as $P \to \infty$ and as $n\,\Delta\omega$ approaches the running variable

ω. Further, we define the spectral density function $g(\omega)$ as $\lim\limits_{P \to \infty} (2\pi D_n/\omega_1)$. The result is

$$f(x) = \frac{1}{2\pi} \int_{-\infty}^{+\infty} g(\omega)e^{i\omega x}\, d\omega, \qquad g(\omega) = \int_{-\infty}^{+\infty} f(x)e^{-i\omega x}\, dx. \quad \text{(A–10)}$$

In this form $f(x)$ and $g(\omega)$ are said to be Fourier transform pairs.* It is a simple matter to show the orthogonality relation

$$\int_{-\infty}^{+\infty} e^{i(\omega-\omega')x}\, dx = 2\pi\, \delta(\omega - \omega'). \quad \text{(A–11)}$$

A–3 Fourier theory in two dimensions

Formally these results can all be extended to two (or more) dimensions. We list here only the more important relations. For the two dimensional form of the complex Fourier series, we have

$$f(x, y) = \sum_{n=-\infty}^{\infty} \sum_{m=-\infty}^{\infty} D_{mn}e^{2\pi i(mx/P_x)+(ny/P_y)}, \quad \text{(A–12)}$$

where

$$D_{mn} = \frac{1}{P_x P_y} \int_{-P_x/2}^{+P_x/2} \int_{-P_y/2}^{+P_y/2} f(x, y)e^{-2\pi i(mx/P_x)+(ny/P_y)}\, dx\, dy.$$

In passing to the two-dimensional Fourier integral, we obtain

$$f(x, y) = \frac{1}{4\pi^2} \iint\limits_{-\infty}^{+\infty} g(\omega_x, \omega_y)e^{i\boldsymbol{\omega}\cdot\mathbf{r}}\, d\omega_x\, d\omega_y,$$

$$g(\omega_x, \omega_y) = \iint\limits_{-\infty}^{+\infty} f(x, y)e^{-i\boldsymbol{\omega}\cdot\mathbf{r}}\, dx\, dy, \quad \text{(A–13)}$$

where $\boldsymbol{\omega} \cdot \mathbf{r}$ refers to the scalar product $\omega_x x + \omega_y y$.

---

* There is an extensive literature on the rigorous theory of the Fourier transform. The most important result is that every square integrable function $f(x)$ has a square integrable Fourier transform $g(\omega)$, which is unique almost everywhere. The Fourier transform of this function $g(\omega)$ is a function which is almost everywhere equal to $f(x)$. Since the majority of functions occurring in physics are square integrable, this theorem and its consequences covers most applications. [See, for example, E. C. Titchmarsh, *Introduction to the Theory of Fourier Integrals* (New York, Oxford Univ. Press, 1948).]

The application of Fourier transforms to the δ-function and similar functions can be justified by the use of distribution theory. [See, for example, H. J. Lighthill, *Introduction to Fourier Analysis and Generalized Functions* (New York, Cambridge Univ. Press, 1960).]

There is one important relation which deserves further consideration. Suppose we transform (ω_x, ω_y) and (x, y) to polar coordinates (ω, ϕ) and (r, θ), respectively. Suppose further that $f(r)$ and $g(\omega)$ possess rotational symmetry (as is often the case in optics) so that the integrals must be independent of θ and ϕ. Equation (A–13) under these circumstances becomes

$$f(r) = \frac{1}{4\pi^2} \int_0^\infty \int_0^{2\pi} g(\omega) e^{i\omega r \cos(\theta-\phi)} \omega \, d\omega \, d\phi,$$

$$g(\omega) = \int_0^\infty \int_0^{2\pi} f(r) e^{-i\omega r \cos(\theta-\phi)} r \, dr \, d\theta.$$

(A–14)

Recalling for a moment the generating function for the Bessel functions

$$e^{\rho/2[t-(1/t)]} = \sum_{n=-\infty}^{\infty} J_n(\rho) t^n,$$

we see that by setting $t = i e^{i(\theta-\phi)}$, we obtain

$$e^{i\rho \cos(\theta-\phi)} = \sum_{n=-\infty}^{+\infty} i^n J_n(\rho) e^{in(\theta-\phi)}$$

so that by integrating both sides from 0 to 2π on θ, we obtain the integral representation of the zero order Bessel function,

$$J_0(\rho) = \frac{1}{2\pi} \int_0^{2\pi} e^{i\rho \cos(\theta-\phi)} \, d\theta.$$

Thus when it is clear that rotational symmetry exists for physical problems, the two-dimensional Fourier transforms in Eq. (A–13) reduce to the Bessel transform pair

$$f(r) = \frac{1}{2\pi} \int_0^\infty g(\omega) J_0(\omega r) \omega \, d\omega,$$

$$g(\omega) = 2\pi \int_0^\infty f(r) J_0(\omega r) r \, dr.$$

(A–15)

A–4 The convolution theorem

The Fourier transform has a number of important theorems associated with it. By far the most important is the convolution theorem for the transform of a product. We shall confine our attention here to one-dimensional time functions, it being understood (both here and throughout the text) that the result can directly be applied to two-dimensional spatial variations.

Consider now the problem of determining

$$F(\omega) = \int_{-\infty}^{+\infty} f_1(t)f_2(t)e^{-i\omega t}\, dt. \tag{A-16}$$

Substituting, for $f_1(t)$ and $f_2(t)$, the Fourier integral representation in terms of $F_1(\omega)$ and $F_2(\omega)$, we have

$$F(\omega) = \frac{1}{(2\pi)^2} \iiint_{-\infty}^{+\infty} F_1(\gamma)F_2(\sigma)e^{-i(\omega-\gamma-\sigma)t}\, d\gamma\, d\sigma\, dt. \tag{A-17}$$

The integral over t represents the integral representation of the delta function so that

$$F(\omega) = \frac{1}{2\pi} \iint_{-\infty}^{+\infty} F_1(\gamma)F_2(\sigma)\delta(\gamma - \omega + \sigma)\, d\gamma\, d\sigma. \tag{A-18}$$

By integrating over γ and making use of the sifting property of the delta function, we have, finally,

$$\int_{-\infty}^{+\infty} f_1(t)f_2(t)e^{-i\omega t}\, dt = \frac{1}{2\pi} \int_{-\infty}^{+\infty} F_1(\omega - \sigma)F_2(\sigma)\, d\sigma. \tag{A-19}$$

This relation is known as the convolution or folding (German, *Faltung*) theorem for the Fourier transform of a product. It is important to realize that a difference [3] exists between a convolution integral and a finite correlation integral. In the convolution integral one of the functions is folded back and then shifted. For time filters, for example, where the causality condition must be satisfied, this is essential. On the other hand, for many optical problems, the functions are symmetric and so the distinction dissolves.

Had we included complex functions in our scheme of things, then Eq. (A-19) would become

$$\int_{-\infty}^{+\infty} f(t)f_2^*(t)e^{-i\omega t}\, dt = \frac{1}{2\pi} \int_{-\infty}^{\infty} F_1(\omega + \sigma)F_2^*(\sigma)\, d\sigma. \tag{A-20}$$

A special case of this complex multiplication theorem occurs when $\omega = 0$, then we arrive at Parseval's theorem

$$\int_{-\infty}^{\infty} f_1(t)f_2^*(t)\, dt = \frac{1}{2\pi} \int_{-\infty}^{\infty} F_1(\sigma)F_2^*(\sigma)\, d\sigma. \tag{A-21}$$

Further, if $f_1(t) = f_2(t)$, this becomes

$$\int_{-\infty}^{+\infty} |f_1(t)|^2 \, dt = \frac{1}{2\pi} \int_{-\infty}^{\infty} |F_1(\sigma)|^2 \, d\sigma. \qquad \text{(A–22)}$$

This expression often represents a conservation principle. In optical diffraction, for example, it merely accounts for the fact that all the light passing through the aperture eventually appears distributed throughout the diffraction pattern. In quantum mechanics it represents a conservation of probability.

A–5 The sampling theorem

Although used in interpolation theory earlier by Whittaker, Shannon has brought the sampling theorem to the attention of modern communication theorists. Essentially the sampling theorem represents a curve fitting device which introduces no error for functions with a definite Fourier cutoff centered around zero frequency. We shall attempt now to demonstrate the sampling theorem and, at the same time, illustrate the use of the convolution theorem. Eventually we shall be interested in optics, so we now switch from time t to space x as the independent variable with the dimensions of mm, for example.

The sampling theorem states that: "If a function $f(x)$ contains no frequencies higher than R cycles per mm, it is completely determined by giving its ordinates at a series of points spaced $1/2R$ mm apart, the series extending throughout the space domain." To demonstrate this remarkable theorem, we shall consider the spectrum of $f(t)$ as the product of a periodic $F_p(\omega)$ and rect ω so that $F(\omega) = F_p(\omega)$ rect ω satisfies the conditions of the sampling theorem (Fig. A–2). We now have for $f(x)$

$$f(x) = \frac{1}{2\pi} \int_{-\infty}^{+\infty} F_p(\omega) \text{ rect } \omega \; e^{i\omega x} \, d\omega. \qquad \text{(A–23)}$$

Now since $F_p(\omega)$ is periodic, we have

$$F_p(\omega) = \sum_{n=-\infty}^{+\infty} D_n e^{-i(n\omega/2R)}, \qquad \text{(A–24)}$$

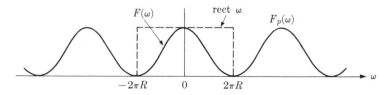

FIGURE A–2

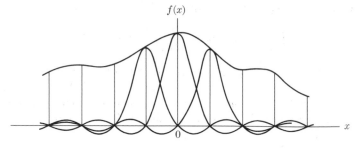

FIGURE A–3

where

$$D_n = \frac{1}{4\pi R} \int_{-2\pi R}^{2\pi R} F_p(\omega) e^{i(n/2R)\omega} \, d\omega$$

$$= \frac{1}{4\pi R} \int_{-\infty}^{+\infty} F(\omega) e^{i(n/2R)\omega} \, d\omega$$

$$= \frac{1}{4\pi R} \, 2\pi f\left(\frac{n}{2R}\right). \tag{A–25}$$

Now substituting this expression for D_n into Eq. (A–24) and the entire sum into Eq. (A–23), we have

$$f(x) = \frac{1}{4\pi R} \sum_{n=-\infty}^{+\infty} f\left(\frac{n}{2R}\right) \int_{-\infty}^{+\infty} \text{rect } \omega \; e^{i[x-(n/2R)\omega]} \, d\omega. \tag{A–26}$$

The Fourier transform of the rect function is well known and leads to the result

$$f(x) = \sum_{n=-\infty}^{+\infty} f\left(\frac{n}{2R}\right) \frac{\sin(2\pi Rx - n\pi)}{2\pi Rx - n\pi} \tag{A–27}$$

In short this theorem states that a sender in Philadelphia wishing to relay a message $f(x)$ to a receiver in Boston need not transmit the entire curve but merely a set of ordinates separated by $1/2R$. Assuming they both know the spectral extent of the message, the receiver in Boston could then construct the original message perfectly* by wrapping $\sin x/x$ functions about each of the sampled ordinates. From the periodicity of this

---

* The reader should be aware that this figurative example violates the very spirit of information theory. The transmission of every message is accompanied by noise. One must take into account not only bandwidth limitations, but also the extent to which these unpredictable fluctuations impair the ability of the receiver from distinguishing one sampled ordinate from its neighbor.

sampling function, it is seen that they do not contribute to the sum at any sampling point other than the one about which it is centered. The Fourier description merely emphasizes that nothing is happening at a faster rate than $1/2R$ (Fig. A–3).

The extension of the sampling theorem to two dimensions is straight-forward and results in the form,

$$f(x, y) = \sum_m \sum_n f\left(\frac{m}{2R_x}, \frac{n}{2R_y}\right) \text{sinc } (2\pi R_x x - n\pi) \text{ sinc } (2\pi R_y y - n\pi),$$
$$(A\text{–}28)$$

where sinc x stands for $\sin x/x$. In many problems of optical interest, the functions and the frequency cut-off possess rotational symmetry. For such cases Gabor [6] and Gamo [7] have demonstrated the circularly symmetric sampling theorem.

Before closing this section, it would be well to emphasize an important point concerning terminology. Throughout this book, the term *correlation* has been reserved to denote an average taken over time, space, or an ensemble. On the other hand, the term *convolution* has been used in connection with the operation of taking the Fourier transform of a product. For real functions, there is no ambiguity. However, for complex functions we have continued to use the term convolution, although no actual folding of the functions takes place, as shown in Eq. A–20. For this reason, the transfer function for incoherent illumination is described as the self-convolution of the complex aperture function, starting in Chapter 5 and continuing throughout the rest of the book. Finally, in all expressions involving the resolution limit and sampling intervals, it has been assumed that the medium is air. Otherwise one must include the index of refraction of the medium in all equations involving the numerical aperture.

References

1. L. A. Pipes, *Applied Mathematics for Engineers and Scientists*. McGraw-Hill (1958).

2. A. Papoulis, *The Fourier Integral and Its Applications*. McGraw-Hill (1962).

3. Y. W. Lee, *Statistical Theory of Communication*. Wiley (1960).

4. C. E. Shannon and W. Weaver, *The Mathematical Theory of Communication*. Univ. of Illinois Press (1949).

5. E. T. Whittaker, Research Paper 8. Univ. of Edinburgh Math. Dept. (1935).

6. D. Gabor, *Progress in Optics*, Vol. 1. E. Wolf, editor. North-Holland (1961).

7. H. Gamo, *J. Opt. Soc. Am.* **47**, 976 (1957) and **48**, 126 (1958).

Probability and Entropy Theory

B–1 The binomial, Poisson, and normal distribution

In this appendix we list some of the more important results of probability and entropy theory which are used in the main body of the text. Let us start with the binomial distribution used in the checkerboard model of Chapter 7. We wish to determine the probability $P_N(m)$ that in a population of N black and white, but otherwise indistinguishable, squares, there will be exactly m white squares. Clearly there are N positions available for the first white square, $N - 1$ for the second, and so on down to $N - m + 1$ positions available for the mth white square. The total number of permutations of the m elements among the N position is then

$$N(N - 1)(N - 2) \cdots (N - m + 1) = \frac{N!}{(N - m)!}, \quad \text{(B–1)}$$

but since the m squares are indistinguishable, the number of combinations of m indistinguishable elements among the positions is

$$C_m^N = \frac{N!}{m!(N - m)!}. \quad \text{(B–2)}$$

However, each of the m squares has a probability $\mathcal{P}$ of occurring, and the $N - m$ black squares have a probability $(1 - \mathcal{P})$. We have then

$$P_N(m) = \frac{N!}{m!(N - m)!} \mathcal{P}^m (1 - \mathcal{P})^{N-m}. \quad \text{(B–3)}$$

It is an elementary exercise to show, for the binomial distribution, that

$$\overline{m} = \sum_{m=0}^{N} m P_N(m) = \mathcal{P}N,$$

$$\overline{m^2} = \sum_{m=0}^{N} m^2 P_N(m) = (\overline{m})^2 + \overline{m}(1 - \mathcal{P}), \quad \text{(B–4)}$$

so that

$$\sigma^2 = \overline{(m - \overline{m})^2} = \overline{m^2} - (\overline{m})^2$$
$$= \mathcal{P}N(1 - \mathcal{P}).$$

Now, if N is allowed to become large [1] while $\mathcal{P}$ becomes small, in such a way that $\overline{m} = \mathcal{P}N$ remains finite, it can be shown, that the binomial distribution approaches the Poisson distribution in the form

$$P_N(m) \cong \frac{(\overline{m})^m e^{-\overline{m}}}{m!},$$ (B-5)

where

$$\overline{m} = \mathcal{P}N,$$
$$\sigma = \sqrt{\overline{m}}.$$

Further, if N continues to get large while y^3/σ^* remains small where

$$y = \frac{m - \mathcal{P}N}{\sqrt{\mathcal{P}N(1 - \mathcal{P})}} = \frac{m - \overline{m}}{\sigma},$$

then we arrive at the normal or Gaussian distribution

$$P_N(m) = \frac{1}{\sqrt{2\pi\sigma^2}} e^{-(m-\overline{m})^2/2\sigma^2}.$$ (B-6)

B-2 The concept of entropy

Let us turn now to a more general situation for which there are N exhaustive, mutually exclusive, and equally likely cases to occur and, of these, n_i are favorable to the event i. We define $\mathcal{P}_i = n_i/N$ as the probability of the occurrence of the ith event. Clearly $\mathcal{P}_i$ is a *linear* measure of our *a priori* uncertainty concerning the outcome ranging from $0 \leq \mathcal{P}_i \leq 1$. Suppose, further, that we associate with each i event, a quantity x_i, then in a long run the average value or expectation value of x is determined by weighting x_i with the frequency of occurrence of the ith event in the form

$$\mathcal{E}(x) = \overline{x} = \sum_{i=1}^{N} x_i \mathcal{P}_i,$$ (B-7)

and, in fact, for any of the moments,

$$\mathcal{E}(x^n) = \overline{x^n} = \sum_{i=1}^{N} x_i^n \mathcal{P}_i,$$ (B-8)

the most common of which involve the mean $\overline{x}$ and the variance

$$\sigma^2 = \overline{(x - \overline{x})^2} = \overline{x^2} - \overline{x}^2.$$

---

* Meaning that we confine our attention around the peak of the distribution.

FIGURE B-1

In addition to $\mathcal{P}_i$, itself, it is often useful to have a stronger measure of the unexpectancy of an event ranging not over a scale from 0 to 1, but from 0 to ∞ and which, for independent events (for example, the toss of a coin in Boston and the turn of a card in San Francisco), satisfies an addition law. A stronger measure that satisfies these conditions is $\log 1/\mathcal{P}_i$. Since this measure so satisfies our intuitive notions concerning the amount of "information" we gain when learning of the occurrence of the ith event, it has been defined in modern communication theory as

$$I_i = \log_2 \frac{1}{\mathcal{P}_i} \tag{B-9}$$

in bits, where the base 2 has been chosen to conform to the standard of counting in binary digits (bits). The average of this quantity over a long sequence is again determined by weighting it with the frequency of occurrence of the ith event and is herewith defined as the "entropy" of the probability distribution $\mathcal{P}_i$,

$$H = - \sum_{i=1}^{N} \mathcal{P}_i \log_2 \mathcal{P}_i = \overline{\log \frac{1}{\mathcal{P}_i}}. \tag{B-10}$$

Using Lagrange multipliers on the always present constraint $\sum_i \mathcal{P}_i = 1$, it is not hard to show that $H_{\max} = \log_2 N$ and occurs when all the $\mathcal{P}_i$'s are equal, $\mathcal{P}_i = 1/N$. If only one event j can occur with certainty, then

$$H_{\min} = 0, \quad \begin{cases} \mathcal{P}_i = 1, & i = j, \\ \mathcal{P}_i = 0, & i \neq j. \end{cases} \tag{B-11}$$

Figure B-1 corresponds to a basic situation in communication [2] theory. A message x constituting a series of i symbols is sent, and the sequence of symbols j make up the received message. We define:

the unconditional probabilities, $\mathcal{P}(i)$ and $\mathcal{P}(j)$;

the conditional probabilities, $\mathcal{P}_i(j) \equiv$ the probability of j given i, $\mathcal{P}_j(i) \equiv$ the probability of i given j;

and the joint probability $\mathcal{P}(i,j) \equiv$ probability of occurrence of i and j.

These probabilities satisfy the set of equations

$$\sum_i \mathcal{P}(i) = 1, \qquad \sum_j \mathcal{P}(j) = 1, \qquad \sum_i \sum_j \mathcal{P}(i,j) = 1,$$

$$\mathcal{P}(i) = \sum_j \mathcal{P}(i,j), \qquad \mathcal{P}(j) = \sum_i \mathcal{P}(i,j),$$

and

$$\mathcal{P}(i,j) = \mathcal{P}(i)\mathcal{P}_i(j) = \mathcal{P}(j)\mathcal{P}_j(i). \tag{B-12}$$

With each of these probabilities, we associate the following:
unconditional entropies:

$$H(x) = -\sum_i \mathcal{P}(i) \log \mathcal{P}(i),$$

$$H(y) = -\sum_j \mathcal{P}(j) \log \mathcal{P}(j),$$

conditional entropies:

$$H_y(x) = -\sum_i \sum_j \mathcal{P}(i,j) \log \mathcal{P}_j(i),$$

$$H_x(y) = -\sum_i \sum_j \mathcal{P}(i,j) \log \mathcal{P}_i(j),$$

and joint entropy:

$$H(x,y) = -\sum_i \sum_j \mathcal{P}(i,j) \log \mathcal{P}(i,j),$$

which satisfy the set of equations

$$H(x,y) = H(x) + H_x(y) = H(y) + H_y(x),$$

or

$$H(x,y) \leq H(x) + H(y);$$

the equality holding when x and y are statistically independent.

Suppose now a single i is sent and j received, how much "information" is transmitted? The information transmitted is just the difference in levels of ignorance before and after transmission. More precisely,

$$I_{i \to j} = \log_2 \left(\frac{a\ posteriori\ \text{probability}}{a\ priori\ \text{probability}} \right).$$

From the sender's point of view,

$$_sI_{i \to j} = \log_2 \frac{\mathcal{P}_i(j)}{\mathcal{P}(j)}, \tag{B-13}$$

while from the receiver's point of view

$$_RI_{i \to j} = \log_2 \frac{\mathcal{P}_j(i)}{\mathcal{P}(i)}. \tag{B-14}$$

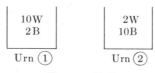

<figure>Figure B–2</figure>

However, from Eq. (B–12)

$$\frac{\mathcal{P}_i(j)}{\mathcal{P}(j)} = \frac{\mathcal{P}(i, j)}{\mathcal{P}(i)\,\mathcal{P}(j)} = \frac{\mathcal{P}_j(i)}{\mathcal{P}(i)}, \tag{B–15}$$

indicating, $_SI_{i\to j} = {}_RI_{i\to j}$, that the quantity of "information" transmitted does not depend upon the observer. Let us now average this expression over all input and output symbols,

$$\overline{I} = \sum_i \sum_j \mathcal{P}(i, j) \log_2 \frac{\mathcal{P}(i, j)}{\mathcal{P}(i)\,\mathcal{P}(j)}. \tag{B–16}$$

A little manipulation and this can be cast into the form

$$\overline{I} = H(x) - H_y(x), \tag{B–17}$$

from the receiver's viewpoint, or equivalently,

$$\overline{I} = H(y) - H_x(y), \tag{B–18}$$

from the sender's viewpoint. In terms of the initial $[H(x)]$ and final $[H_y(x)]$ states of ignorance concerning the message that was sent, Eq. (B–17) can be written as

$$H_y(x) = H(x) - \overline{I} \tag{B–19}$$

so that an increase in $\overline{I}$ is a decrease in $H_y(x)$. Of course, in the absence of "noise," $H_y(x) = 0$.

As an illustration of these ideas, consider the example of two urns (Fig. B–2). The first contains 10 white and 2 black balls; the second contains 2 white and 10 black balls. A ball is drawn from the first and, color unknown, is placed in the second urn whose contents are then mixed. A ball is then drawn from the second urn and its color noted. At this point the urns are restored to their original state by an observer and the whole process is repeated. How many bits-selection are transmitted through this system? Let W_1 and B_1 correspond to the events of drawing a white or a black ball, respectively, from urn 1 and depositing it in urn 2; this is the "message sent." Let W_2 and B_2 correspond to the events of subsequently choosing a white or a black ball from urn 2; this is the "message received." Now by the definitions of the various probabilities and the theorems of total and compound probability, we can construct the following probability table.

Message sent: i	W_1	W_1	B_1	B_1
Message received: j	W_2	B_2	W_2	B_2
$P(i, j)$	$\frac{15}{78}$	$\frac{50}{78}$	$\frac{2}{78}$	$\frac{11}{78}$
$P(i)$	$\frac{5}{6}$	$\frac{5}{6}$	$\frac{1}{6}$	$\frac{1}{6}$
$P(j)$	$\frac{17}{78}$	$\frac{61}{78}$	$\frac{17}{78}$	$\frac{61}{78}$
$P_j(i)$	$\frac{15}{17}$	$\frac{50}{61}$	$\frac{2}{17}$	$\frac{11}{61}$
$P_i(j)$	$\frac{3}{13}$	$\frac{10}{13}$	$\frac{2}{13}$	$\frac{11}{13}$
$I_{i \rightarrow j} = \log_2 \dfrac{P(i, j)}{P(i)P(j)}$	$\log_2 \frac{18}{17}$	$\log_2 \frac{60}{61}$	$\log_2 \frac{12}{17}$	$\log_2 \frac{66}{61}$

$$\overline{I} = \sum_i \sum_j I_{i \rightarrow j} P(i, j) = H(x) - H_y(x) = H(y) - H_x(y)$$

$$= \tfrac{50}{78} \log_2 \tfrac{60}{61} + \tfrac{15}{78} \log_2 \tfrac{18}{17} + \tfrac{11}{78} \log_2 \tfrac{66}{61} + \tfrac{2}{78} \log_2 \tfrac{12}{17}$$

$$= 0.0318 - 0.0289$$

$$= 0.0039 \text{ bits/selection.}$$

Entropy in the continuous case. For continuous probability distributions one can define* conditional, unconditional, and joint entropies in the form

$$H(x) = -\int \mathcal{P}(x) \log \mathcal{P}(x)\, dx,$$

$$H(y) = -\int \mathcal{P}(y) \log \mathcal{P}(y)\, dy,$$

$$H_y(x) = -\iint \mathcal{P}(x, y) \log \mathcal{P}_y(x)\, dx\, dy,$$

$$H_x(y) = -\iint \mathcal{P}(x, y) \log \mathcal{P}_x(y)\, dx\, dy,$$

$$H(x, y) = -\iint \mathcal{P}(x, y) \log \mathcal{P}(x, y)\, dx\, dy.$$

---

* These equations are obviously not correct dimensionally. The difficulty stems from the fact that the term $\lim_{\Delta x \to 0} \log \Delta x$ appears when making the transition from the discrete to the continuous case. In practice the important results in information theory involve differences in entropy taken over the same metric so that terms such as this drop out. As a matter of principle, however, since every measurement in physics yields a finite amount of information, Δx can only approach $\Delta x_{\min}$, the interval within which we can, at best, assign a uniform distribution due to the limiting resolution of an instrument. Moreover, in quantum statistical mechanics, the uncertainty principle absolutely forbids us to pass to a smaller volume in phase space than h^3.

We have already seen, in the discrete case, the limits achieved by $H(x)$ subject only to the condition $\int \mathcal{P}(x)\, dx = 1$. Suppose now, in addition, we fix one of the moments in the form

$$\int_{-\infty}^{\infty} x^n \mathcal{P}(x)\, dx = \text{const.}$$

Again invoking the method of Lagrange multipliers and setting $\delta H = 0$, one can show that H assumes its maximum value when

$$\mathcal{P}(x) = A e^{-\beta x^n}, \tag{B–20}$$

where A and $\mathcal{B}$ are chosen to satisfy the two constraint equations. In physics, for $x = E$, the total energy of a system, $n = 1$ and Eq. (B–20) represents the Boltzmann distribution. For $x = v$, the velocity of a gas molecule, $n = 2$, and Eq. (B–20) represents the Maxwell-Boltzmann velocity distribution law for an ideal classical gas. To paraphrase Woodward [2], for a fixed mean square value, the Gaussian distribution is the most random of all; random in the sense of maximum entropy. From this point on all the results developed by Shannon [3] for channel capacity, entropy loss in a linear filter etc. can be carried over directly to optics [4], [5] with suitable extension to two dimensions.

B–3 The illumination matrix in the coherent limit

In Chapter 8 an attempt was made to relate the concepts of coherence and entropy. There we demonstrated that the diagonalized illumination matrix does, in fact, assume for the coherent and incoherent limits the form corresponding to minimum and maximum entropy, respectively. Let us start with the expression

$$B_{mn} = \iint u_m^*(\xi_2)\Gamma(\xi_1,\,\xi_2)u_n(\xi_1)\, d\xi_1\, d\xi_2.$$

In this section, we are concerned primarily with the statistical structure of the *light*, not the effect of the object or lenses. Hence, we can reduce this equation to a description of the light alone by first setting the complex transmission of the object equal to a constant C everywhere, and then by setting

$$u_n(\xi_1) = \delta\left(\xi_1 - \frac{n}{2W}\right)$$

to remove the effect of the lenses. Equation (8–27) then reduces to

$$B_{mn} = \Gamma_{mn} = \Gamma\left(\frac{m}{2W},\frac{n}{2W}\right). \tag{B–21}$$

In the incoherent limit $\Gamma_{mn} = C^2 \, \delta_{mn}$ which is already in diagonal form. We now choose the constant such that $\sum_{i=1}^{N} \lambda_i = 1$, and so we have for incoherent light

$$\Lambda = \begin{pmatrix} 1/N & & & & \\ & 1/N & & & 0 \\ & & 1/N & & \\ & & & 1/N & \\ & 0 & & & \ddots \end{pmatrix} \tag{B-22}$$

corresponding to maximum entropy.

In the coherent limit

$$\Gamma_{mn} = C^2 = 1/N,$$

and we now wish to solve for the eigenvalues from the determinant equation

$$|\mathbf{B} - \mathbf{\Lambda}| = 0, \tag{B-23}$$

which can always be written [4] as a polynomial in λ in the form

$$\lambda^n + C_1 \lambda^{n-1} + C_2 \lambda^{n-2} + \cdots C_n = 0, \tag{B-24}$$

where

$$C_1 = -S_1,$$
$$C_2 = -\tfrac{1}{2}(C_1 S_1 + S_2),$$
$$\vdots$$
$$C_n = -\frac{1}{n}(C_{n-1}S_1 + C_{n-2}S_2 + \cdots C_1 S_{n-1} + S_n),$$

and where

$$S_n = \mathrm{Tr}\, \mathbf{B}^n.$$

Now for the particularly simple form of the $\mathbf{B}$ matrix in the coherent limit, one can see directly that

$$\mathbf{B}^2 = \mathbf{B},$$

and, in fact,* that

$$\mathbf{B}^n = \mathbf{B}.$$

We thus have

$$C_1 = -S_1 = -\mathrm{Tr}\, \mathbf{B} = -1, \tag{B-25}$$
$$C_n = 0, \qquad n > 1,$$

---

*Students of quantum mechanics will recognize this expression for $\mathbf{B}$ as a projection operator. The eigenvalues then follow directly from the matrix equation $\mathbf{B}^{n-1}(\mathbf{B} - 1) = 0$.

so that the secular equation becomes

$$(\lambda^n - \lambda^{n-1}) = 0 = \lambda^{n-1}(\lambda - 1), \tag{B-26}$$

indicating a diagonalized matrix of the form

$$\Lambda_{\text{coherent}} = \begin{pmatrix} 0 & & & & & \\ & 0 & & & 0 & \\ & & 1 & & & \\ & & & 0 & & \\ 0 & & & & 0 & \\ & & & & & 0 \\ & & & & & & \ddots \end{pmatrix}. \tag{B-27}$$

REFERENCES

1. T. C. FRY, *Probability and its Engineering Uses.* D. Van Nostrand (1928).

2. P. M. WOODWARD, *Probability and Information Theory.* McGraw-Hill (1953).

3. C. E. SHANNON and W. WEAVER, *The Mathematical Theory of Communication.* Univ. of Illinois Press (1949).

4. E. H. LINFOOT and P. B. FELLGETT, *Trans. Roy. Soc.* (London) A **247**, 369 (1955).

5. G. TORALDO DI FRANCIA, *Optica Acta,* **2**, 5 (1955).

6. H. BÔCHER, *Introduction to Higher Algebra.* The Macmillan Co. (1931).

Index

INDEX

ABCDE69876543